Accent on ALGEBRA
REVISED

Pat Boyle

WITH
BILL JUAREZ

Creative Publications, Inc.

© 1977 Creative Publications, Inc.
P. O. Box 10328
Palo Alto, California 94303
Printed in U.S.A.

ISBN: 0-88488-046-X

TABLE OF CONTENTS

WELL, LET'S GET STARTED!!

INTRODUCTION TO SECOND EDITION

The ACCENT here is on ALGEBRA! It is possible to misjudge the appearance of this collection of activities. They are, on first examination, light-hearted diversions. Look closer and you discover that the activities take a good deal of good algebra to complete. That is, the ACCENT is on the ALGEBRA. ACCENT ON ALGEBRA attempts to flavor the usual work in an unusual way. The unusual assignment formats enliven the work with a fresh, enriching, and entertaining spirit.

Each activity was designed for the average algebra student and has been used with classes at various levels from junior high school to college, wherever elementary algebra is offered. Many of the activities were used to review elementary topics with advanced groups. Wherever they were used they were successful in replacing the usual activities in the course, successful in supplementing and complementing the material of the course, but most importantly successful in motivating algebra students with a real sense of participation.

SUGGESTIONS FOR USING ACCENT ON ALGEBRA

ACCENT ON ALGEBRA may be used with any level algebra student or in any course where algebraic topics are introduced and used. In upper elementary school, junior and senior high school, and junior college there are areas in which the appropriate puzzle or activity from ACCENT ON ALGEBRA will contribute to the course. I will not presume to tell you when and how to use the materials with your classes. Each teacher has a different way of integrating supplementary activities into the work. I have used these materials as well as more conventional ones and other devices of my own design. The combination has successfully and substantially flavored my classes to produce a lively atmosphere, the kind of environment in which students developed favorable attitudes that positively affected their achievement. My experience has been with secondary and college students in California schools, but I feel certain that algebra students everywhere will react similarly.

ACCENT ON ALGEBRA is specially designed to be reproduced for classroom use. Spirit or mimeograph reproduction should expand the usefulness of the book considerably. The following suggestions are offered to maximize this potential.

1. Masters may be made directly from most pages to run student copies. You may add your own directions or hints by writing in India ink on the page before producing the master or by typing directly on the master after production. In any case, be sure to check the master before running student copies to see that the directions are adequate for your group and that it will not prove necessary to explain some of the terms and phrases used. The Glossary on page 124 lists some of the special types of numbers used in the activities.

2. Transparencies are very helpful in correction and discussion. You may project these on a screen or chalkboard for class discussion and correction or lay them over student work as correction keys. First, prepare a transparency directly from the page, then write answers on the film with a film marker. If you want them to be more permanent, mark the answers on a separate sheet with India ink (or other high-carbon medium) and rerun the film adding the answers to the transparency. You might want to run the answers on a separate film (color is very effective) to use as an overlay.

3. Since the pages of ACCENT ON ALGEBRA are made to be removed and copied, I suggest you remove all the pages and store them in a sturdy three-ring binder. Place index tabs on the chapter title pages so that pages may be more easily located. Chapter Previews are on the back of each title page. As you make and use transparencies and spirit masters, you can file them in the binder for later reuse.

4. Many of the activities in ACCENT ON ALGEBRA lend themselves to the use of a calculator, but each instructor must decide when the calculator is appropriate. The Chapter Previews make note of certain activities that may be appropriate but no page contains any remark to that effect. Whether a calculator is used or not, the mathematics is still the focus, the algebra the accent. Where a calculator is not available, tables of powers and roots may be advisable. A table of primes is provided on page 126.

ACTIVITY FORMATS

Each chapter begins with a brief summary of the activities for that topic. The Chapter Preview is on the back of the title page for the chapter. Notes and comments here may assist you in your choice from the selection available. Of course, there is no substitute for actually working the exercise yourself to get a feeling for its difficulty and appropriateness. On the basis of this experience, you may find it necessary to supplement directions or substitute problems for a particular class. Since free use is made of certain special numbers, a glossary and a table of primes have been added to the second edition.

Nine assignment formats are listed in the table of contents. It may be helpful to say a few words about each here at the outset.

1. ALGEBRA ADAGES

An *Algebra Adage* is a disguised proverb. The student must unravel statements like "a rotating fragment of minerals collects no bryophytic plants" into "a rolling stone gathers no moss." The letters of the words in the *Adage* are found from clues supplied by solving an equation or answering a question. The total activity provides many cross-checks. The letter patterns of English words alert the solver to possible errors. An RQZT will indicate immediately that something is amiss. Because the student is aware something is wrong, there is an opportunity to correct problems as they arise instead of waiting for the next class meeting. Cross-checks are also built into the problems themselves. A common error in one problem will very likely produce the answer to the very next problem. The student is faced with resolving this obvious discrepancy before proceeding and repeating the error. This popular activity is a self-checking assignment, in that the student will know if he or she is successful. In many cases, the student will have worked out his or her own difficulties before returning to class, or questions will be more focused, more specific, leading to better use of class time.

2. CROSSWORD PUZZLES

Each chapter contains one *Crossword Puzzle* and, while they are like the ones in the daily paper, they are different, too. The primary objective of their design was to use a maximum number of words from the vocabulary of the chapter. Once these words were arranged, number words and other related words were used to expand the puzzle. Only then was consideration given to completing the remainder and making the array as dense as possible. As a result, there are many nonsense and hybrid "words" that could only be eliminated by sacrificing the mathematical vocabulary. Many of the clues are tongue-in-cheek and you must do a couple before you get into the spirit of things. While these activities and others listed later involve very little algebraic manipulation, they provide much needed vocabulary work. Many mathematics students have their greatest difficulty with the language of the subject. Through a series of word activities, ACCENT provides added experience which should prove a definite aid. In designing these activities, it was found that students usually liked them and that many discovered the dictionary is more than a book of short, short stories.

3. CROSSNUMBER PUZZLES

Crossnumber Puzzles are in crossword format with digits replacing letters and numbers replacing words. An advantage of this type of activity is the cross-checks built into the overlapping design of the puzzle. An immediate feedback of this kind allows the student to catch errors and correct them as the assignment is being completed. There are two distinctly different kinds of these puzzles in ACCENT. The orthodox, exercise type are included. However, there are also more interesting and challenging inferential types. By inferential I mean that the clues may be interdependent—to complete an entry from a clue, other clues may have to be worked out first or at least consulted.

4. CROSSNOMIAL PUZZLES

Using the crossword/crossnumber format, algebraic expressions with numbers, variables, and signs of operation may occupy the squares. Again there is the cross-check and feedback of an *Adage* or a *Crossnumber Puzzle*. A challenging aspect is provided by the commutativity of the elements of each term *and* of the terms themselves. Even though the numerical coefficient is always first, there are still quite a number of arrangements for most polynomials. Note carefully the instructions for the first *Crossnomial* on page 28.

5. ALPHAMETICS

An *Alphametic* is an arithmetic problem with digits replaced by letters of the alphabet. In each problem, each letter will stand for a particular but different digit. Few youngsters seem to have encountered this type of problem and *Alphametics* are a good test of understanding of concepts and algorithms. They also provide chances to apply new algebraic concepts. A full page introduction to this activity is provided on page 18, prior to the first *Alphametics* page. You may be surprised at which students take the challenge of this particular activity.

6. MATCHSTICKS

It is said the puzzlemaker's best friend is a matchstick. *Matchsticks* lend themselves to the playing of math games and to the demonstration of feats of equilibrium, arithmetic and algebraic puzzles, and geometric puzzles and illusions. ACCENT has disguised and presented some geometric puzzles and other oddities along with some more familiar material. The *Matchsticks* are the unifying medium for the puzzles found throughout the book.

7. ALGEBRA SEARCHES

Modeled after the popular word searches in newspapers and magazines, these activities provide still more vocabulary experience. Like their newspaper counterparts, the *Searches* come in two formats. One is an array of letters that spell out mathematical terms vertically, horizontally, and diagonally. The other format is similar except you may start with any letter and jump to any adjacent letter, continuing until a word is spelled. Unlike the larger array, you may change direction and weave through this array to spell the term.

8. PALATABLE PLOTTING

This graphing activity is another self-checking format in which the student is able to recognize success and identify errors and examine them. The set of equations or inequalities when graphed correctly will form a complete picture. Since the picture is the payoff, neatness, attention to detail, and accuracy become much more important. If you find the graphing activities effective with your classes, you may want to examine two other books devoted exclusively to similar exercises: *Graph Gallery* and *Palatable Plotting*. *Graph Gallery* is designed for elementary algebra students and *Palatable Plotting* is for more advanced students.

9. SCRAMBLES

The *Scrambles* pages are a combination of two different vocabulary puzzles. The more common is simply a permutation of the letters of the word or phrase to spell a different word or phrase. Usually called *anagrams,* these are the easier of the two. The second type is a word *rebus.* Elementary children may see quite a few picture *rebuses,* such as:

  for BOOK + WORM or bookworm. You rarely see a rebus that goes beyond this level. *Accent* substitutes words (instead of pictures) for mathematical terms or syllables or letters of mathematical terms. These rebuses tend to be more difficult than the picture type, so many students discover a dictionary.

ACKNOWLEDGEMENTS

I must acknowledge the encouragement and cooperation of my present colleagues Joe Smyth, Carol Olmstead, Dick Giles, Milt Hoehn, and Karl Smith. They have provided helpful suggestions and exposed the exercises to the appropriate audience. A note of thanks to Bob Fairbanks at Comstock Jr. H.S. in Santa Rosa, Trude McCulloch, Rick Keller, and Skip Curtis at Piedmont Hills H.S. in San Jose, Fran Smith at James Lick H.S. in San Jose, Frank Burrows of the East Side Union H.S. District, and to the many people with whom I have talked at conferences and meetings. Their feedback (and backtalk) certainly flavored the final result. Special thanks to Lyn Savage, Project Editor at Creative Publications, for her valuable contributions during this revision.

Ultimately, I must thank my students. Those who asked if I had more, or an extra copy for a friend, or just said they enjoyed doing them. Their positive attitude was a great satisfaction and gratification. Thanks also to those who said, "Ahhhh, not that stuff again . . . Hey, ya got any more?" and to the student who told a friend, "He just gets 'em outa some book!" Special thanks to that occasional student who constructed an original to put me to the test. And certainly those who were unmoved by my creations or my efforts to reach them, and inspired me to continue to look for attractive and enjoyable activity formats, and more interesting ways to present the material in class.

And now I thank *you* for your interest. I hope you will have successful experiences using ACCENT ON ALGEBRA with your students. Further, I hope you attempt to design some of your own activities to focus on special areas of particular concern. If you do come up with something, or have comments, criticisms, complaints, compliments, corrections, . . . I would very, very much enjoy hearing from you.

Patrick J. Boyle
Sebastopol, California
October 1, 1976

Sets & Properties

ALGEBRA ADAGE

$$\underline{}\ \underline{}\ \underline{}\ \underline{}\ \underline{}\ \underline{}\ \ \overset{S}{\underline{}}\ \ \underline{}\ \underline{}\ \underline{}\ \underline{}\ \underline{}\ \underline{}\ \underline{}\ \underline{}\ \underline{}\ \underline{}\ \ \underline{}\ \underline{}\ \underline{}\ \underline{}\ \underline{}\ ,$$

d u d a n a   d r g w s y w a d o   s n g e u

$$\underline{}\ \underline{}\ \underline{}\ \ \underline{}\ \underline{}\ \underline{}\ \ \underline{}\ \underline{}\ \underline{}\ \underline{}\ \ \underline{}\ \underline{}\ \underline{}\ \overset{S}{\underline{}}\ \ \underline{}\ \ \underline{}\ \underline{}\ \underline{}\ .$$

x e k   g w y   j g n y   j d v y   d   j g x

MATCH THE SETS DESCRIBED ON THE LEFT WITH THE SETS LISTED ON THE RIGHT AND REPLACE THE SMALL LETTER IN THE PUZZLE ABOVE (IF IT APPEARS) WITH THE CAPITAL LETTER WHICH CORRESPONDS.

A = The set of one-digit odd numbers.
B = The subset of all perfect squares in S.
C = The set of all primes in S.
D = The set of odd numbers between three and seven, inclusive.
E = The set of numerals whose spellings are three letters long.
F = The set of even numbers at least as large as two and at most equal to ten.
G = The set of numerals whose names can be spelled using a subset of [I, F, H, E, S, T, R, O, N, G].
H = The set of numbers which are unchanged by being "flipped" up-side-down.
I = The set of even numbers between one and ten.
K = The set of even composites in S.
L = The set of numerals whose spellings use three distinct letters.
M = The set of digits occurring in the decimal for the fraction one-seventh.
N = The set of numerals used in the title of Orwell's classic futuristic novel.
O = The set of all multiples of three in S.
P = The subset of S which contains multiples of three which are multiples of five.
Q = The subset of S which contains odd numbers at least as large as five or primes less than seven.
R = The set of all perfect cubes in S.
T = The set of numbers whose numerals are drawn exclusively with straight line segments.
U = The set of numerals whose English spelling contains exactly four different letters.

S = {1,2,3,4,5,6,7,8,9,10}
a = {2,4,6,8}
b = {4,5,9}
c = {1,3,8,10}
d = {1,3,5,7,9}
e = {3,4,5,7}
f = {3}
g = {3,6,9}
h = {1,6,8,9}
i = {1,3,6,8,9,10}
j = {1,2,4,5,7,8}
k = {1,4,7}
l = {3,5,7}
m = {1,7}
n = {1,8}
o = {1,2,6,9,10}
p = {2,3,5,7,9}
q = {5}
r = {2,3,5,7}
s = {1,3,8,9,10}
t = {1,8,9}
u = ∅
v = {4,6,8,10}
w = {1,4,8,9}
x = {1,4,9}
y = {1,2,6,10}
z = {2,4,6,8,10}

NOW, WHAT IS THE FAMILIAR PROVERB THAT IS HIDDEN IN THE ALGEBRA ADAGE ABOVE?

$$\underline{}\ \underline{}\ \underline{}\ \underline{}\ \underline{}\ \underline{}\ !$$

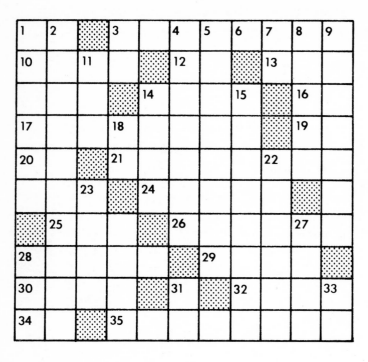

YOU'LL LIKE THIS
CROSSWORD PUZZLE
MANY OF THE CLUES DEAL WITH THE TOPIC OF SETS. OTHER CLUES, WELL . . . .

ACROSS

1. Fe, fi, __?__ , fum
3. Objects contained in a set
10. Notion
12. Bushel, abbr.
13. Scat!
14. Ø = __?__ set
16. Backfield position, abbr.
17. Indefinite, uncountable
19. Elements of the set of letters in the word sees.
20. Element of $\{$ to, two, too. . . $\}$
21. Half liberated
24. $\{$ $\}$ but not $\{$Ø$\}$ or $\{$0$\}$
25. Large
26. $\{$747, 727, 707. . .$\}$
28. Element of $\{$3, 7, 8, 50, 60$\}$
29. Height above sea level, abbr.
30. Angered
31. 100
32. Finished
34. More than one X
35. $\{$1, 2, 3. . . $\}$ is the set of ____?____ Numbers.

DOWN

1. Countable
2. $\{$1, 3, 5, 7 . . . $\}$ (2 words)
3. Per
4. Elements of $\{$B, U, M, P, I, E$\}$
5. If a = b·c, then a is a ____?____ of b and c.
6. Vowel
7. Nova Scotia, abbr.
8. See 28 ACROSS
9. Ø, $\{$1$\}$, $\{$2$\}$, $\{$3$\}$, $\{$1,2$\}$, $\{$1,3$\}$, $\{$2,3$\}$, and $\{$1,2,3$\}$
11. Dwarf
14. Elements of $\{$N, E$\}$
15. Much remains (3 words)
18. =
22. Elements of $\{$I, E, N, V, Y, R$\}$
23. Element of $\{$0, 4, 5, 9$\}$
27. Multiple of two
28. Element of $\{$1, 2, 6, 10$\}$
31. Cubic, abbr.
33. Football lineman, abbr.

HERE IS AN ADAGE WHOSE CLUES CONTAIN SYMBOLS OF GROUPING, PARENTHESES, BRACKETS, AND BRACES, WITH: $3 + 9 \div 3 \times 2 + 2 \times 6 \div 3$

A = $3 + \left\{ [(9 \div 3) \times (2 + 2)] \times (6 \div 3) \right\}$ = _____

C = $[(3 + 9) \div 3] \times 2 + [(2 \times 6) \div 3]$ = _____

D = $(3 + 9) \div \left\{ [(3 \times 2) + (2 \times 6)] \div 3 \right\}$ = _____

E = $(3 + 9) \div [3 \times (2 + 2) \times (6 \div 3)]$ = _____

F = $3 + [9 \div (3 \times 2)] + (2 \times 6 \div 3)$ = _____

H = $3 + 9 \div \left\{ [(3 \times 2) + (2 \times 6)] \div 3 \right\}$ = _____

I = $3 + [(9 \div 3) \times 2] + (2 \times 6 \div 3)$ = _____

L = $(3 + 9) \div [(3 \times 2) + (2 \times 6 \div 3)]$ = _____

M = Twice the value of one of these expressions if no symbols of inclusion were used. = _____

N = $\left\{ (3 + 9) \div [3 \times (2 + 2) \times 6] \right\} \div 3$ = _____

O = $\left\{ 3 + 9 \div [3 \times (2 + 2)] \right\} \times (6 \div 3)$ = _____

R = $3 + \left\{ 9 \div [(3 \times 2) + (2 \times 6 \div 3)] \right\}$ = _____

S = $3 + \left\{ 9 \div [3 \times (2 + 2) \times (6 \div 3)] \right\}$ = _____

T = $\left\{ 3 + [(9 \div 3) \times 2] + (2 \times 6) \right\} \div 3$ = _____

Y = $\left\{ 3 + [9 \div (3 \times 2)] + (2 \times 6) \right\} \div 3$ = _____

__ __ __ __ __ __ __**U** __ __ __ __ __ __ __ __ __ __ __ __**U** __
$7\frac{1}{2}$ $\frac{1}{18}$ $\frac{1}{2}$ 3.9 $\frac{1}{2}$ 2 $8\frac{1}{2}$ 3.9   13 7 $7\frac{1}{2}$ $8\frac{1}{2}$ 7 $4\frac{1}{2}$ $\frac{1}{2}$ 26 27 1.2 $3\frac{3}{8}$

__ __ __ __ __ __**G** __ __ __ __ __ __ __ __ __ __ __ __ __
$8\frac{1}{2}$ 27 26 13 1.2 $5\frac{1}{2}$ 13 $\frac{1}{18}$ $\frac{1}{2}$ $3\frac{3}{8}$ 7 $\frac{1}{2}$ 2   2 27 13 1.2 $5\frac{1}{2}$ $4\frac{1}{2}$ $7\frac{1}{2}$ 1.2 2 $3\frac{3}{8}$

__ __ __ __ __ __ __ __ __ __ __ __**P** __ __ __ __ __ __ .
27 26 $\frac{1}{2}$ 2 13 12 27 1.2   2 13 $3\frac{3}{8}$ 12 13   1.2 $\frac{1}{2}$ 27 $8\frac{1}{2}$ 27 3.9

NOW, TRANSLATE THE ALGEBRA ADAGE ABOVE INTO A COMMON PROVERB BELOW.

__ __   __ __ __ __ __   __   __ __ __   __ __ __ __

__ __ __   __ __ __ __ __   __ __ __ __ __ .

Here is a little different

CROSSNUMBER PUZZLE.

That is, no one clue will give an answer. Good luck, anyway! !

Wayne had a busy weekend, and here he tells about himself, his family, and the weekend in his Beetle. The information should be enough to fill in the puzzle.

ACROSS

1. His older brother's age
3. His father's age
5. The year of his Volks
7. The number of gallons of gas that he used
9. His father's age when Wayne was thirteen
12. The square of his father's age
14. The distance he drove in two hours, at his average speed
15. His average miles-per-gallon gas consumption

DOWN

1. The total distance he drove, in miles
2. 8 DOWN - 3 ACROSS
4. A number which is increased by nine when the digits are reversed
5. Half of Wayne's age
6. His average speed, in miles-per-hour
8. The distance driven in three hours at that speed
9. The square of his average miles-per-gallon
10. Another number like 4 DOWN
11. Twice his older brother's age
13. Wayne's age

ALGEBRA ADAGE

GIVEN THAT a = 2, b = 5, x = 3, AND y = 4, FIND THE VALUE OF EACH OF THE FOLLOWING TO COMPLETE THE ADAGE BELOW BY REPLACING THE NUMBER CLUE BY THE LETTER WITH THAT VALUE.

$\overline{21}\ \overline{6}\ \overline{0}\ \overline{21}\ \overline{8}\ \overline{2}\ \overline{12}$ $\overline{0}\ \overline{21}\ \overline{9}\ \overline{1}$ $\overline{6}\ \overline{12}\ \overline{4}\ \overline{1}\ \overline{6}\ \overline{21}\ \overline{8}\ \overline{25}\ \overline{2}\ \overline{12}\ \overline{G}$

$\overline{Y}\ \overline{9}\ \overline{4}\ \overline{21}$ $\overline{7}\ \overline{9}\ \overline{4}\ \overline{5}\ \overline{25}\ \overline{21}$ $\overline{Y}\ \overline{7}\ \overline{21}\ \overline{2}\ \overline{9}\ \overline{21}$ $\overline{25}\ \overline{9}$

$\overline{25}\ \overline{3}\ \overline{6}\ \overline{2}\ \overline{21}$ $\overline{6}\ \overline{1}\ \overline{6}\ \overline{21}\ \overline{G}$ $\overline{6}\ \overline{12}\ \overline{22}\ \overline{6}$ $\overline{0}\ \overline{21}\ \overline{9}\ \overline{1}$ $\overline{25}\ \overline{3}\ \overline{6}\ \overline{2}\ \overline{21}$

$\overline{22}\ \overline{8}\ \overline{5}\ \overline{22}\ \overline{2}\ \overline{0}\ \overline{2}\ \overline{6}\ \overline{D}$ $\overline{6}\ \overline{12}\ \overline{22}\ \overline{5}\ \overline{9}\ \overline{S}\ \overline{4}\ \overline{21}\ \overline{6}\ \overline{S}.$

A = a + b – x + y

C = 5a + 4b – 2y

E = $\frac{2b + a}{3} + \frac{y}{2}$

F = (b – a) (x + y) (2a – y)

H = b^2 – xy – ab

I = $\frac{ax + by}{ab + x}$

L = $\frac{y}{a} + \frac{b + y}{x}$

M = [a(b – x) – y] + [x(y – a) – b]

N = xy^2 + x^{2}y^2 – [x^{2}y + (xy)^2]

O = b(x^2 + y^2) – y(a^2 + b^2)

P = $\frac{(x + y)b^4}{(axy)^2 + (a + b)^2}$

R = x^2 + y^2 – a^2

T = (x + y –a)^2

U = $\frac{xy}{a} - \frac{b + x}{y}$

NOW, WHAT IS THE COMMON PROVERB PARAPHRASED IN THE ALGEBRA ADAGE?

____ _____ ____ _____

_____ ____ ____.

ALPHAMETICS

An Alphametic presents the regular layout of a simple arithmetical calculation—addition, subtraction, multiplication or division—but with the digits changed into letters of the alphabet. In each puzzle each letter will stand for a particular but different digit. The solver must discover the digital values of the letters, and so find the original calculation.

```
  SEND
+ MORE
 MONEY
```

SEND MORE MONEY is the first known example of an Alphametic. It supposedly is an urgent message from a coed at college to her parents.

```
  SEND
  1ORE
 1ONEY
```

First, note that M must be 1 since S and M are added and M is carried to the last place in the sum.

```
  9END
  10RE
 10NEY
```

Next it is reasoned that S must be 9 and O is zero. (Why?)

Then notice N will always be one more than E. (Why?)

Since E and N occur several times, we try values for E and N. As we do, we notice that N + R must be at least ten. (Why?)

```
  956D
  10R5
 1065Y
```

E = 5 and N = 6 are the first to work. (Notice each E is replaced by a 5.)

```
  9567
  1085
 10652
```

Finally, the original problem is restored. Notice that it was a mixture of reasoning, and trial and error that produced the answer.

S = 9	M = 1
E = 5	O = 0
N = 6	R = 8
D = 7	Y = 2

In 1931 the name "Cryptarithm" was used for such puzzles in the recreational mathematics magazine *Sphinx*. But at that time most cryptarithms were a meaningless jumble of letters. In 1955, J.A.H. Hunter coined a new word "Alphametic" for those cryptarithms in which words and even phrases would appear such as the SEND MORE MONEY puzzle above. In fact, the following Alphametics were a continuation of the SEND MORE MONEY correspondence. See if you can solve the two responses.

```
     HE
   SENT
     HE
   SENT
    THE
+  TEN
  THEN
```

```
   SEND
+  MORE
  MONEY
```

```
   ALAS
   LASS
+   NO
  CASH
```

18

ALL OF THESE ALPHAMETICS INVOLVE NUMBER WORDS. YOU'LL NOTICE THE WORD ARITHMETIC IS CORRECT IN EACH CASE, AND THE NUMBER ARITHMETIC YOU ARE TO DISCOVER IS ALSO CORRECT.

```
    Z E R O
    O N E
+   T W O
---------
  T H R E E
```

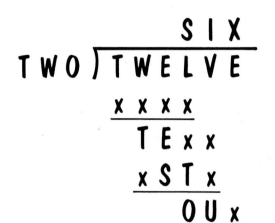

```
              S I X
T W O ) T W E L V E
          x x x x
          T E x x
          x S T x
            O U x
            x T x
              x x
```

```
    T W O
  T H R E E
+ S E V E N
-----------
T W E L V E
```

```
      O N E
      T W O
+   F I V E
-----------
  E I G H T
```

```
  F O R T Y
    T E N
+   T E N
---------
S I X T Y
```

THIS IS AN. . . .

ALGEBRA SEARCH

IT CONTAINS AT LEAST 50 WORDS DEALING WITH SETS, NUMBERS AND PROPERTIES.

THE WORDS ARE ARRANGED VERTICALLY, HORIZONTALLY AND DIAGONALLY!!

```
                    S
                  N Y
                I O M
              N I I M
            E N N T E
          S C I T U T
          S L X N E T R
          E U A E F R I I
        N S S M S I S T C
        N I S E V R N E S E
      E O O C Q U E I C B I
      E N C A W E N V T T U G
    W H I L R S B L N E I S H
    T N A P N E N Z I I T O E T
    E N T E I O B S E K N W N H X
    B E I R B A I M V R E P O R P
    V V U L R N N E F O U R E X
    E V I T A T U M M O C E I
    V R N R C E T D D L U S
    I E Y A E R O D O N U
    T F T N S M R S L N
    U L I S A S U I I
    B E T I W R K Q
    I X N T E E U
    R I E I E E
    T V D V N
    S E I E
    I F S
    D S
    W
```

HEH, HEH!! DUPLICATES AND WORDS FROM OTHER TOPICS. . . . DON'T COUNT!

FRONTWARDS AND !OOT SDRAWKCAB

20

SCRAMBLES

THE FIRST SIX PHRASES BELOW ARE MADE UP OF THE LETTERS OF A MATHEMATICAL TERM. RE-ARRANGE THE LETTERS TO FIND THE TERM WHICH HAS BEEN SCRAMBLED.

TAME OR RUN IS A SCRAMBLE OF NUMERATOR, SEE?

1. SAM LENT A FUND

2. VICE AT OASIS

3. SCOUT BIN RAT

4. STRIVE IT BUDI

5. LEER IF VEX

6. QUITE NAVEL

WORD REBUSES

NUMBER 7 IS AN EXAMPLE OF A REBUS. A REBUS IS A WORD PUZZLE IN WHICH EACH CLUE SUGGESTS A WORD OR SYLLABLE OF A MATH TERM. NOT ALL ARE AS EASY AS THE EXAMPLE!!!

7. UMPIRE + MALE NICKNAME + I HAVE

R E F   L E X   I V E

8. ME + BUMP + THAT + WHY

— — — — — — — — — —

9. TIME* + RACED + POSE + FOUR + EAST*

— — — — — — — — — — —

10. DISTANCE* + TEASE + U + T + I HAVE

— — — — — — — — — —

*Abbreviation

21

Integers

Chapter Preview - Integers

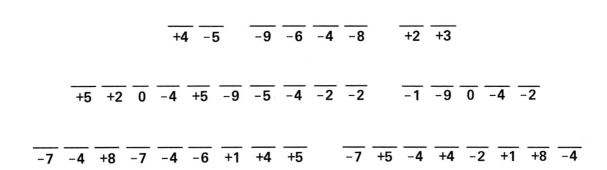

$$\overline{}_{+4}\ \overline{}_{-5} \qquad \overline{}_{-9}\ \overline{}_{-6}\ \overline{}_{-4}\ \overline{}_{-8} \qquad \overline{}_{+2}\ \overline{}_{+3}$$

$$\overline{}_{+5}\ \overline{}_{+2}\ \overline{}_{0}\ \overline{}_{-4}\ \overline{}_{+5}\ \overline{}_{-9}\ \overline{}_{-5}\ \overline{}_{-4}\ \overline{}_{-2}\ \overline{}_{-2} \qquad \overline{}_{-1}\ \overline{}_{-9}\ \overline{}_{0}\ \overline{}_{-4}\ \overline{}_{-2}$$

$$\overline{}_{-7}\ \overline{}_{-4}\ \overline{}_{+8}\ \overline{}_{-7}\ \overline{}_{-4}\ \overline{}_{-6}\ \overline{}_{+1}\ \overline{}_{+4}\ \overline{}_{+5} \qquad \overline{}_{-7}\ \overline{}_{+5}\ \overline{}_{-4}\ \overline{}_{+4}\ \overline{}_{-2}\ \overline{}_{+1}\ \overline{}_{+8}\ \overline{}_{-4}$$

FIND THE VALUE OF EACH OF THE CAPITAL LETTERS BELOW. REPLACE THE VALUES ABOVE BY THE CORRESPONDING LETTER AND DISCOVER THE ALGEBRA ADAGE.

$A = [(-2)^3 - (-1)\,(-2)\,(-3)]^2$

$E = \dfrac{|-1| - [(-2) - (-3)\,(-4)] - (-5)}{-(6 - (-7)) - (-8)}$

$F = 1 - (-2) + 3|4 - (5 + 6) + 7|$

$G = 4(-3) + 21 \div 3 + 4$

$I = 4(-3) + 21 \div (3 + 4)$

$L = -(-1)\,[(-2) - 3(-4)] - 5[(-6) - (-7)]$

$M = |-1| - (-2) - 3(-4) - (-5)\,(-6) - (-7)$

$N = -\dfrac{(-1) - (-2)\,(+3)\,(-4)}{-5}$

$O = \dfrac{(-1)\,(-2)\,[3 - (-4)]}{6 - 7 - (-8)}$

$P = |1 - 2|\,[(-3)^3 + (-4)\,(-5)]$

$R = (-2)^5 + (-3)4(-5) + (-6)^2 - (-7)\,(-8)$

$S = (-2)^3\,(-3)^3 - (-4)^3 + 5^3 - |-6| + (-7)^2\,(-8) + (-9)$

$T = (-1)\,(-2)\,(-3)\,(-4)\,(-5) - [\,|-6|\,(-7) - (-8)\,(-9)]$

$U = (-1) - 2\,(-3)\,(-4) - (-5)\,(-6) - 7(-8)$

$V = 4 - (3 + 21) \div 3 + 4$

NOW THAT YOU HAVE DISCOVERED THE ALGEBRA ADAGE FROM THE CLUES, REPHRASE IT IN A MORE COMMON FORM.

CROSSWORD PUZZLE

HERE'S A PUZZLE WITH AN EMPHASIS ON INVERSES AND NEGATIVES.

ACROSS

1. Guarantees an answer

4. Poverty

7. Therefore

8. $a - b = (a) \ ? \ (-b)$

9. Inverse of many

10. Positive on a vertical scale

11. Plus or minus

12. The greater of the number and its additive inverse (2 words)

15. Mister

16. Yes!

17. No!

18. Inverse of 4 DOWN

21. Name abbreviation

23. Liquid 22 DOWN

24. Inverse of veteran

25. Opposite or reciprocal

26. Gave up

DOWN

1. Military unit, abbr.

2. Additive inverse

3. u^4

4. Inverse of 18 ACROSS

5. Permutation of DOWNLINE

6. Positive or negative

7. Overload

9. $|6 + 18 \div 3 - 7 + 8 \times 2 - 19| + 3$

10. Inverse of them

11. $|10 + 25 \div 5 - 6 \times 2 + 5 - 15|$

13. Tanned

14. 1,0567 quarts

19. Southern Association of Animal Doctors, abbr.

20. Governmental tax outfit

22. Solid 23 ACROSS

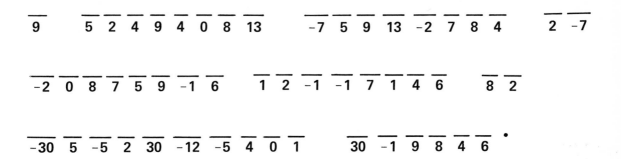

$$\overline{}_{9} \quad \overline{}_{5}\ \overline{}_{2}\ \overline{}_{4}\ \overline{}_{9}\ \overline{}_{4}\ \overline{}_{0}\ \overline{}_{8}\ \overline{}_{13} \quad \overline{}_{-7}\ \overline{}_{5}\ \overline{}_{9}\ \overline{}_{13}\ \overline{}_{-2}\ \overline{}_{7}\ \overline{}_{8}\ \overline{}_{4} \quad \overline{}_{2}\ \overline{}_{-7}$$

$$\overline{}_{-2}\ \overline{}_{0}\ \overline{}_{8}\ \overline{}_{7}\ \overline{}_{5}\ \overline{}_{9}\ \overline{}_{-1}\ \overline{}_{6} \quad \overline{}_{1}\ \overline{}_{2}\ \overline{}_{-1}\ \overline{}_{-1}\ \overline{}_{7}\ \overline{}_{1}\ \overline{}_{4}\ \overline{}_{6} \quad \overline{}_{8}\ \overline{}_{2}$$

$$\overline{}_{-30}\ \overline{}_{5}\ \overline{}_{-5}\ \overline{}_{2}\ \overline{}_{30}\ \overline{}_{-12}\ \overline{}_{-5}\ \overline{}_{4}\ \overline{}_{0}\ \overline{}_{1} \quad \overline{}_{30}\ \overline{}_{-1}\ \overline{}_{9}\ \overline{}_{8}\ \overline{}_{4}\ \overline{}_{6}\ .$$

GIVEN THAT u = –1, v = 2, w = –3, AND x = –5, FIND THE VALUE OF EACH OF THE FOLLOWING CAPITAL LETTER VARIABLES. REPLACE THE VALUES ABOVE BY THE CORRESPONDING LETTERS TO DISCOVER THE ALGEBRA ADAGE.

A = _____ = $u^2 + v^3$

B = _____ = $uvwx$

C = _____ = $u(v + w)$

E = _____ = $x - 2vw$

F = _____ = $u + v + w + x$

G = _____ = $uv + wx$

H = _____ = $u + vw + x$

I = _____ = $|x| + (w - v)$

L = _____ = $-(x - vw)$

$w^3 + x^2$ = _____ = M

$(w + x)u$ = _____ = N

$\dfrac{x + u}{w}$ = _____ = O

vwx = _____ = P

$x(v^3 - w^2)$ = _____ = R

$wx^2 + w^4$ = _____ = S

$\dfrac{v^3 w}{x + u}$ = _____ = T

$-|x|$ = _____ = Y

NOW THAT YOU HAVE DONE THE EASY PART, SEE IF YOU CAN PARAPHRASE THE ALGEBRA ADAGE AS A WELL-KNOWN PROVERB.

1	2	3	4	5	6	7	8
9							
10							
11							░
12							13
14						░	
15						░	
16				░	17		

CROSSNOMIAL PUZZLE

Each square contains exactly one sign, digit, or variable character. Thus $-4x + xy - 32$ is entered as:

−	4	X	+	X	Y	−	3	2

or the variables may be permuted as:

−	4	X	+	Y	X	−	3	2

or the terms may be permuted as:

−	3	2	−	4	X	+	Y	X

Notice the coefficient, if one, is not entered.

ACROSS Simplify each expression.

1. $(x + y - 5) - (6x - y + 7)$

9. $(x + y) + (2y + 3) + (z + y) + (y + 2)$

10. $-xz(1 + 3y)$

11. $x - 3(3z - 2y)$

12. $3y(1 + 2z) - 2(y - 2x)$

14. $y - 2\{x + 3(x - y)\}$

15. $z(3 + 2y)$

16. $-2x(-3yz)$

17. $x\{y - y(1 - z)\}$

DOWN Simplify each expression.

1. $2\{x - 3(y + 6)\}$

2. $y(1 + 3x) - 2x(y - 4z)$

3. $4(y - z) - 3(x + y) - (x + z)$

4. $5(y - x) - 2(2x - z)$

5. $z + 2(z + 3y) + (x + y)$

6. $-zy(1 - 6x)$

7. $xy(1 + z) - x(y - z) - z(x - y) - (yz - 1)$

8. $5\{5 + 5(x - 1)\}$

13. $(x - 2y) - (z + 2y) - (2y + x) - 2(y - z)$

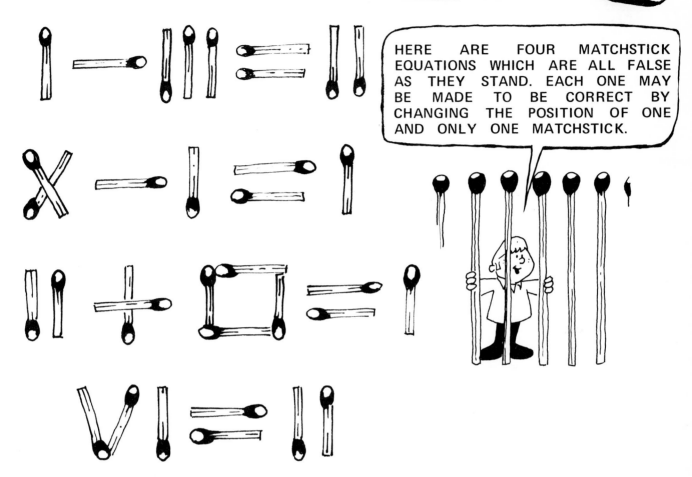

HERE ARE FOUR MATCHSTICK EQUATIONS WHICH ARE ALL FALSE AS THEY STAND. EACH ONE MAY BE MADE TO BE CORRECT BY CHANGING THE POSITION OF ONE AND ONLY ONE MATCHSTICK.

ALPHAMETICS

	TRIAL		TEST		MORE
	AND		ALL		MORE
	ERROR		THE		MORE
	AT		ALPHA		IN
	RANDOM		METICS		FORM

THERE **IS** A UNIQUE SOLUTION TO THIS BIT OF POOR ADVICE.

YOU DO, DON'T YOU?

LOOK FOR A LEFT-OVER BICENTEN-NIAL SOLUTION.

IN EACH ALPHAMETIC, EACH LETTER STANDS FOR A DIFFERENT DIGIT. TEST YOUR UNDERSTANDING OF ADDITION ON THESE THREE. IN SPITE OF THE ADVICE, TRIAL AND ERROR SHOULD NOT BE RANDOM. CAREFUL INVESTIGATION IS MORE IN FORM.

ACROSS

1. Fourth term of 4, 77, 150
4. 2[2 DOWN] + [26 ACROSS]
7. [9 ACROSS] + [26 ACROSS]
8. [28 ACROSS] + [Weeks in 3/4 of a year]
9. Complement of 68°
10. 23 ACROSS
12. [Days in a year] - [26 ACROSS]
13. Smallest prime factor of 8549
15. Smallest prime factor of 9553
16. The first three digits = [4 ACROSS] - [Days in November]. The last four digits = Einstein's Nobel Prize year.
18. Fifty more than the number of days in six consecutive years
19. The middle two digits equal the square of a prime.
21. Two times a prime
23. Four more than the sixth power of the first odd prime number
24. The product of the first two odd primes
25. A palindromic number in which the last digit is twice the second
26. A prime less than thirty
27. Three times the sum of the 6th and 13th primes
28. Half-dozen times the 37th prime

One additional clue is necessary to complete this puzzle. The digits form a magic square taking the blanks as zeroes.

CROSS NUMBER PUZZLE

DOWN

1. [18 DOWN] + 68
2. The fifty-first prime
3. Seventy-sixth prime, a palindrome
5. Sum of the last two digits equal the first
6. The third digit is twice the second, the fourth is one more than the second, the first is sum of the last two.
11. The second digit is twice each of the last three which are the same, while the first is one less than the last and is prime.
12. A five digit number
14. The number 100a + 10b + c where 2a + c = b
15. 2^4 times the 11th prime
16. A cyclic arrangement of 2, 3, 4, 5 and 6
17. 2[6 DOWN] + [25 ACROSS - 20]
18. A prime in which the last two digits are the same
20. A dozen five hundred twenty-sixes
22. [10] [Weeks in a year] + 24

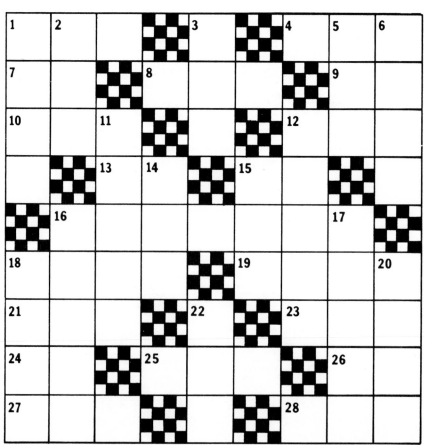

SCRAMBLES

HERE ARE SOME MATHEMATICAL TERMS WHOSE LETTERS HAVE BEEN REARRANGED – 'PERMUTED ACROSS' – TO FORM THE PHRASES YOU SEE.

1. SO, I'VE TIP

2. I GAVE TEN

3. MAUD, GET IN

4. LOU LEAVE AT BUS

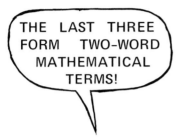

THE LAST THREE FORM TWO-WORD MATHEMATICAL TERMS!

5. WITHIN + STANZA

_ _   _ _ _ _ _ _ _

6. NEON* + PISTOL (SLANG) + I HAVE

_ _ _ _ _ _ _ _

7. POST OFFICE* + BE SEATED + FOUR + EAST*

_ _ _   _ _ _ _   _ _

HERE ARE SOME MORE

WORD REBUSES.

EACH CLUE SUGGESTS A WORD OR A SYLLABLE OR A LETTER OF SOME MATHEMATICAL TERM.

8.† WRITE ONE'S NAME + EDWARD* + DEVOID OF SENSATION + ERBIUM*

_ _ _ _ _   _ _ _ _ _ _   _ _ _

*Abbreviation

†Answer is two words.

Polynomials

SIMPLIFY THE ALGEBRAIC EXPRESSIONS TO DETERMINE THE COEFFICIENTS INDICATED BY THE CAPITAL LETTERS. FILL THE BLANKS BELOW WITH THE CAPITAL LETTERS WHICH CORRESPOND TO THE VALUES SHOWN UNDER EACH BLANK SPACE. . . TO DISCOVER THE

ALGEBRA ADAGE

Row 1:
$$\frac{}{-1}\ \frac{}{8}\ \frac{}{-7}\ \frac{}{7}\ \frac{}{-1}\ \frac{}{7}\ \frac{}{-2}\ \frac{}{4} \qquad \frac{}{3}\ \frac{}{-2}\ \frac{}{2} \qquad \frac{}{-1}\ \frac{}{7}\ \frac{}{5}\ \frac{}{7}\ \frac{}{-2}\ \frac{}{4} \qquad \frac{}{-8}\ \frac{}{7}\ \frac{}{-7}\ \frac{}{-5}$$

Row 2:

$$\frac{}{-9}\ \frac{}{-1}\ \frac{M}{-3} \qquad \frac{}{-9}\ \frac{}{-7}\ \frac{}{7}\ \frac{}{-7}\ \frac{}{6}\ \frac{}{2}\ \frac{}{8} \qquad \frac{}{1}\ \frac{}{-1}\ \frac{}{8}\ \frac{}{3}\ \frac{}{-7}\ \frac{}{8}\ \frac{}{5} \qquad \frac{}{-3}\ \frac{}{-2}\ \frac{}{8}$$

Row 3:
$$\frac{}{-8}\ \frac{}{-5}\ \frac{}{-3}\ \frac{}{7}\ \frac{}{5} \qquad \frac{}{5}\ \frac{}{3}\ \frac{}{-6}\ \frac{}{6}\ \frac{}{-7}\ \frac{}{3}\ \frac{}{-1}\ \frac{Y}{}\ , \qquad \frac{}{-3}\ \frac{}{-9}\ \frac{}{6}\ \frac{}{-6}\ \frac{}{8}\ \frac{}{-2}\ \frac{}{-7}\ ,$$

Row 4:
$$\frac{}{3}\ \frac{}{-2}\ \frac{}{2} \qquad \frac{}{8}\ \frac{}{-1}\ \frac{}{6}\ \frac{}{2}\ \frac{}{7}\ \frac{}{-7}\ \frac{}{8}\ .$$

$3(2 - x) - (3 - 2x) - 2(1 - 2x) = Ax + C$

$2\{(3 + 4y) - [y - 3(1 - y) - (y - 2)]\} = Dy + E$

$2 - z\{z - 5(z - 2) - 5\} = Gz^2 + Hz + D$

$5h - \{3 - [4 - (7 - 2h)]\} = Ih + L$

$\{k - [3 - 2k(1 - k)]\} - 2\{4k - (k - 3)\} = Nk^2 + Ok + P$

$\{(a + 2b) - (3 - b)\} - \{(a + 4) + (a - 2b)\} = Ra + Sb + T$

$m(2m - 3n) - 2n(2m - 3n) = Dm^2 + Tmn + Un^2$

$2[3r(r - s) - s(r - s)] = Ur^2 + Wrs + Ds^2$

$2m(m - 3) + 3n(3 - m) - m(1 - 3n) = Dm^2 + Tm + Wn$

A = _____
C = _____
D = _____
E = _____
G = _____
H = _____
I = _____
L = _____
N = _____
O = _____
P = _____
R = _____
S = _____
T = _____
U = _____
W = _____

WHEN YOU HAVE DISCOVERED THE ALGEBRA ADAGE, THEN YOU SHOULD BE ABLE TO PARAPHRASE THE DISGUISED PROVERB IN ITS MORE COMMON FORM.

CROSSNOMIAL PUZZLE

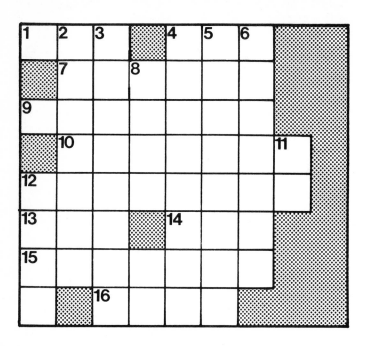

Each square contains exactly one sign, digit, or variable character. Thus $x^2 - 2x + 13$ may be entered as any of:

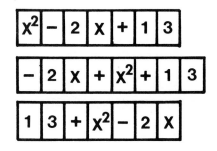

Notice the coefficient, if one, is not entered.

ACROSS

Simplify each expression.

1. $(4x)^2$

4. $11 \cdot 2^5$

7. $(x + 1)(x + 2)$

9. $(x + 5)(x - 7)$

10. $(x - 1)(4x + 9)$

12. $(x - 2)(6x + 17)$

13. $(1 - x)(x^2 + x + 1)$

14. $(14)(x^2) = 14x^2$ or:

15. $(13 + 6x)(2 - x)$

16. See 8 DOWN.

DOWN

Simplify each expression.

2. $(2x - 3)(3x + 2)$

3. $(x - 1)(x + 3) - x^3$

4. $(8x + 1)(3 - 4x) - (3x + 2)(4x + 3)$

5. $(3x + 1)(x + 5)$

6. $(15 - 8x)(15 + 8x)$

8. See 16 ACROSS.

11. $(3x)^2$

12. $(8x)^3$

BUT...THEY MUST... MATCH DOWN AND ACROSS!

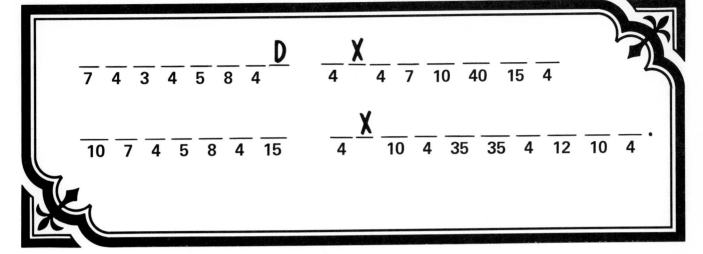

$$\overline{}_{7}\ \overline{}_{4}\ \overline{}_{3}\ \overline{}_{4}\ \overline{}_{5}\ \overline{}_{8}\ \overline{D}_{4}\qquad \overline{X}_{4}\ \overline{}_{4}\ \overline{}_{7}\ \overline{}_{10}\ \overline{}_{40}\ \overline{}_{15}\ \overline{}_{4}$$

$$\overline{}_{10}\ \overline{}_{7}\ \overline{}_{4}\ \overline{}_{5}\ \overline{}_{8}\ \overline{}_{4}\ \overline{}_{15}\qquad \overline{X}_{4}\ \overline{}_{10}\ \overline{}_{4}\ \overline{}_{35}\ \overline{}_{35}\ \overline{}_{4}\ \overline{}_{12}\ \overline{}_{10}\ \overline{}_{4}\ .$$

EACH CAPITAL LETTER BELOW HAS A UNIQUE VALUE.

$(3x + A)\,(2x - P) = 6x^2 + x - S$ A = _____

C = _____

$(3x - E)\,(2x + P) = 6x^2 + x - N$ E = _____

I = _____

$(3x - R)\,(2x + A) = 6x^2 + x - L$ L = _____

N = _____

$(3x - C)\,(2x + R) = 6x^2 + x - 2L$ P = _____

R = _____

$(3x + T)\,(2x - A) = 6x^2 + x - I$ S = _____

T = _____

IF YOU REPLACE THE BLANKS ABOVE BY THE LETTER WHICH CORRESPONDS TO EACH NUMBER, YOU WILL DISCOVER THE HIDDEN ALGEBRA ADAGE. WHEN YOU FINISH, PARAPHRASE THE ALGEBRA ADAGE AS A FAMILIAR PROVERB.

MATCHSTICKS

THIS FALSE EQUATION MAY BE CORRECTED

BY MOVING TWO MATCHES TO NEW POSITIONS.

THE FOLLOWING EQUATIONS MAY BE CORRECTED BY
MOVING ONE AND ONLY ONE MATCH STICK.

1.

3.

2.

4.

5. REMOVE EIGHT MATCHES SO THAT ONLY TWO SQUARES ARE LEFT.

6. SHIFT EXACTLY FOUR MATCHES TO MAKE THREE SQUARES.

7. CHANGE HALF OF THESE TO GET FIVE SQUARES.

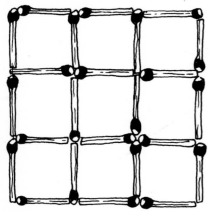

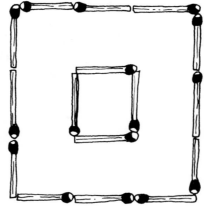

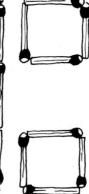

DO IT IN TWO DIFFERENT WAYS.

AND THIS ONE IN TWO WAYS

8. HOW MANY SQUARES DO YOU COUNT IN ALL THE FIGURES ABOVE? MORE THAN FIFTEEN!!

CROSSWORD PUZZLE · · · · · · · · · · · · ·

ACROSS

1. $(x + 5)(x - 1) = x^2 + ?x - 5$
5. Prefix for small or short
9. If $x = 3$, then $2x^3 + 5x^2 - 3x = ?$
11. $(2x + 5)(x + 2) = 2x^2 + ?x + 10$
13. When multiplied, the coefficient of the linear term of $(x + 3)(x + 4)$ is ?
14. Beast of burden
16. Unodd
18. The first palindrome
19. Permutation of ENTICE
21. See 25 DOWN
22. Minus, abbr.
23. The cue (sounds like)
24. Pitch
26. Southern Railway, abbr.
27. The G.C.F. of $12m^2a$, $8ma^2$, $16m^2a^2$ and $32m^3a^2$
30. 2 a ? or ? 4 2
31. East
32. $3x + 1 = 3 + 4x$ and $9x + 4 = 7x$
35. See 41 ACROSS
36. Is a veteran too (3 words)
37. Negative suffix (contraction)
39. ter^2
41. See 21 ACROSS
42. Permutation of VUP HAT
44. An exclamation
45. 17 DOWN minus 53 ACROSS
47. Arrangement
48. Excuses
52. Raw metal
53. $-1 - x^3$ if $x = -2$
54. Permutation of TEN EARS
56. Scary
58. Are
59. A binomial is at least of degree _____ .
60. A Southwestern state (abbr.)
61. Pastries with holes

DOWN

1. $5,000
2. If $x = 6$, then $x^4 - 15x^2 - 4x^3 + 17x + 7 = ?$
3. Together with 5 DOWN is a permutation of MENU
4. Opposite of left (abbr.)
5. See 3 DOWN
6. Opposite of out
7. Daughter of your brother-in-law
8. Earn interest, hopefully
9. In $\dfrac{3q}{x - q}$, x is ?
10. Hither and _____
12. e^2
13. Feel
15. Eleven
17. Find a, if $x = -2$ and $x^3 + 4x^2 + ax + 10 = 0$
19. Statement of equality
20. Reverse, change, shift
23. Peace symbol
25. See 35 ACROSS
27. First degree term of $3t^2 + 5t - 7$
28. Red Letter Association
29. Liquefy
33. Egypt and friends
34. Trip
35. $x - 2$ and $2 - x$
38. When simplified $x[3 + x(x + 2)]$ is a polynomial of degree _____ .
39. Discusses
40. If $x = -1$, then $\frac{1}{2}(x^2 - 5x) = ?$
43. Decorates
46. Permutation of I NEW
49. See 16 ACROSS
50. Ave., Rd., Blvd., or _____ ?
51. Gain by work
55. Negative
57. Edward or editor
62. A vowel
63. Another vowel

40

CROSSNUMBER PUZZLE

THIS UNUSUAL CROSSNUMBER PUZZLE HAS NO DIRECT CLUES. EACH CLUE DEPENDS ON ANOTHER. GOOD LUCK!

ACROSS

1. 11 ACROSS - 22 ACROSS
3. Sum of squares of seven consecutive natural numbers
6. 20 ACROSS + 35 DOWN
8. 6 ACROSS + 18 ACROSS
10. Perfect square
11. Palindromic perfect cube
12. 11 DOWN – 13 DOWN
14. A factorial
15. Perfect number
16. 6 ACROSS + 11 ACROSS
18. 34 ACROSS + 35 DOWN
20. A prime
22. Two digit prime times 20 ACROSS
24. Several baker's dozens
25. Product of digits is perfect cube
27. Product of two consecutive primes
30. Perfect square
32. Largest three-digit prime
34. A palindromic number
35. A prime
36. Product of two consecutive primes
38. Several dozens
39. 32 ACROSS - 25 ACROSS
41. Product of two consecutive primes

DOWN

1. 13th odd prime
2. 37 DOWN + 16 ACROSS
4. Divisor of 11 ACROSS and 30 ACROSS
6. Palindromic number divisible by 9
7. 1, 1, 2, 3, 5, 8, __?__, . . .
9. Another number from the sequence above in 7 DOWN
11. Product of two consecutive primes
13. 3 ACROSS + 24 ACROSS
15. 23 DOWN – 18 ACROSS
17. A perfect number
19. A factorial
21. Five digits of π
23. Number is reduced by 273 when turned up-side-down
26. Product of two consecutive primes
28. 27 ACROSS + 12 ACROSS
31. Not composite
33. A palindromic prime
34. Product of two primes
35. A perfect number
37. Largest two-digit prime
39. Not prime
40. A composite

ALPHAMETICS

DISCOVER THE ORIGINAL PROBLEM FOR EACH
BELOW. EACH LETTER STANDS FOR A UNIQUE
DIGIT.

```
  ANTS
  CAN'T
 _____
  SCAN


  FIRS
  FOR
  THE
 _____
  BIRDS
```

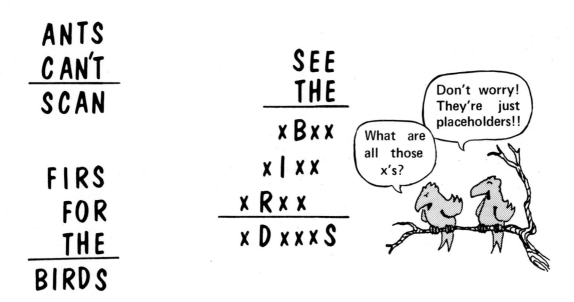

```
   SEE
   THE
  _____
  x B x x
  x I x x
  x R x x
  _____
  x D x x x S
```

AN ALPHAMAZE

MANY NUMBER WORDS ARE HIDDEN IN
THIS ARRAY OF LETTERS. START IN
ANY SQUARE AND MOVE IN ANY DIREC-
TION TO AN ADJACENT SQUARE. FOR
EXAMPLE, Z - E - R - O CAN BE SPELLED
AS SHOWN:

YOU SHOULD FIND n WORDS WHERE
n ≥ 30. THE SAME LETTER CAN BE USED
MORE THAN ONCE IN THE SAME WORD.

Z	R	H	Y
O	E	T	S
I	N	E	W
F	V	L	O

42

SCRAMBLES

TRY SCRAMBLING SOME WORDS OF YOUR OWN... LIKE MONOMIAL! ! !

UNSCRAMBLE THE FOLLOWING TO FIND THE PERMUTATION OF THE LETTERS THAT WILL SPELL A MATHEMATICS WORD FROM THE UNIT.

1. A LIVE BAR

    __ __ __ __ __ __ __ __

2. SCANT TON

    __ __ __ __ __ __ __ __

3. LOAN IT RIM

    __ __ __ __ __ __ __ __ __

4. I MOAN, POLLY!

    __ __ __ __ __ __ __ __ __ __

BOOK + WORM
bookworm

5. ACTUALITY + A CONJUNCTION

    __ __ __ __ __ __ __

6. WAR CAPTIVE + UNIT OF WORK – (GRAM*)

    __ __ __ __ __(__)

Bronx Cheer + Potassium + Anelid
Boo+k +worm
bookworm!

7. VERBALIZE + IODINE* + ATTACHED

    __ __ __ __ __ __ __ __ __ __

8. BISMUTH* + NUMBER* + MILE* + ALUMINUM*

    __ __ __ __ __ __ __ __ __

*Abbreviation

Equations and Inequalities

Chapter Preview - Equations and Inequalities

ALGEBRA ADAGE

SOLVE THE FOLLOWING EQUATIONS FOR SOME HELPFUL CLUES TO THE PUZZLE BELOW. USE THESE CLUES TO COMPLETE THE ALGEBRA ADAGE.

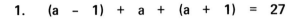

1. $(a - 1) + a + (a + 1) = 27$ a = _____

2. $(b + 1) + (b + 2) + (b + 3) = 45$ b = _____

3. $103 - 4d - 6d = 3$ d = _____

4. $-85 - e + 4e = -25$ e = _____

5. $2f - (f - 1) = 9$ f = _____

6. $7(h - 9) - 3h + 19 = 0$ h = _____

7. $12.5 - 2(i + 2i) = 12.5$ i = _____

8. $4L + \frac{1}{2}(-6 - 2L) - 33 = 0$ L = _____

9. $5(m + 17) - 8(m + 1) - 2 = 0$ m = _____

10. $3(8n - 44) - 3(1 - n) = 0$ n = _____

11. $15o - (3o + 4) - (-3o) = 26$ o = _____

12. $2(2 - 3p) = 9(5 - p) + 1$ p = _____

13. $1 = \frac{2}{3}(9 - r) + 5$ r = _____

14. $1 - \frac{3}{5}(20 - s) = 7$ s = _____

15. $6t^2 - 3(t + 2t^2) + 18 = 0$ t = _____

16. $5z - [z - 2(z - 49) - 3 - z^2] = -(-25 - z - z^2)$ z = _____

— — —   — — — — — — — — —   — — — — — — — —
6 11 20   14 15 2 25 14 6 20 30 6   8 20 9 6 11 20 15 20 10

— — — — —   — — — — — —   — — —   — — — — — — — .
13 0 14 20 10   30 20 0 24 20 30   6 11 20   9 5 5 20 12 0 10

NOW THAT YOU HAVE DONE THE EASY PART, SEE IF YOU CAN SHORTEN THE ALGEBRA ADAGE INTO A WELL-KNOWN PHRASE.

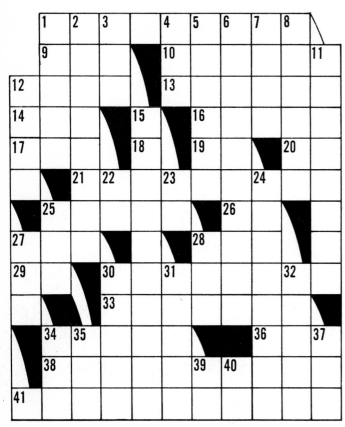

HEY, THE

CROSSWORD

ON THIS PAGE IS
ALL ABOUT EQUATIONS
AND INEQUALITIES! !

ACROSS

1. Positive or negative ____?____
9. Are not (contraction, sort of?)
10. Marvel
12. $3x + 4 < 5x - 6$, then $x >$?
13. The largest of three consecutive integers whose sum is 33
14. $3(x - .2) > x + 1.4$, then ? $< x$
16. 14 ACROSS and 28 DOWN are __?__
17. Ukraine, abbr.
19. Are you
20. District Attorney
21. Waved the stick (three words)
25. Multiplicative inverse, abbr.
26. Consecutive letters
27. Help!
28. Lube
29. That thing
30. Overcast (two words)
33. Needs an Ophthalmologist (2 words)
34. $x - 3(x - 9) = (3x - 4) - 2(x - 5)$; $x = $?
36. Collection
38. One of three integers is two less than the largest and two more than the smallest. Their sum is sixty-nine. What is the largest?
41. If $x - 2 < 3(2x - 1) - 1$, then $2 - x$? $2(3x - 2)$

DOWN

1. Imbibe
2. $+$ & $-$, and x & $\div$
3. Way or course, abbr.
4. Hundred weight, abbr.
5. The tower between F and H
6. Not an equation or an identity
7. Permutation of L O U D
8. State of gambling
11. 16 ACROSS and 41 ACROSS are each a binary ____?____
12. $3(x - 1) + 5 = 2(2x - 1)$, then $x = $?
15. Solving equations is a process of finding successive __?__ equations.
22. Restroom, British
23. Neptunium, chemical symbol
24. Permutation of BLESS HIM
25. Decay
27. $2x + 3 > 15$, then $x >$?
28. $(2x - 3[(x - 2) - 3x] - 5) = 7x$, $|x| = $?
30. $\frac{nx}{5} - a = 0$, then $x = \frac{?}{n}$
32. Advice to veterans (more than 1 word)
34. R Street, abbr.
35. Mama sheep
37. $3(x - 1) - 2(3 - x) - 4x = 1$ then $x = $?
39. Unit of time, abbr.
40. Unit of length, abbr.

48

EACH LETTER HAS A DISTINCT INTEGER VALUE. ALL VALUES CAN BE FOUND FROM THE CLUES BELOW. REPLACE THE BLANKS AT THE BOTTOM BY THE CORRESPONDING LETTER AND DISCOVER THE ALGEBRA ADAGE. THIS TIME IT IS A PUZZLING PROVERB WHICH REQUIRES A LITTLE DEDUCTION TO SOLVE. FINALLY REPHRASE THE ALGEBRA ADAGE AS A COMMON PROVERB.

$BAD + MAN = SAM - IS + MAD + SON$ $\qquad$ A = _____

$\dfrac{1}{2}B + \dfrac{1}{3}B = 5$ $\qquad$ B = _____

$ROD + SOB = B + O - BVD$ $\qquad$ D = _____

$DO + ONE + MORE = D + O$ $\qquad$ E = _____

$MINI + ON = SID\left(\dfrac{NI}{B} + \dfrac{D}{IS} - \dfrac{S - O}{N}\right)$ $\qquad$ I = _____

$BM - V = V^2 M + B$ $\qquad$ M = _____

$DORM + BORN = SNOB - B^2$ $\qquad$ N = _____

$BO - VM = B^2 + SO + V$ $\qquad$ O = _____

$MR(B + VR) = S(MO + O^2 + R^2)$ $\qquad$ R = _____

$\dfrac{BS}{V} - M = B + \dfrac{VS}{M}$ $\qquad$ S = _____

$SEE + IT - IS + DONE - RITE = ISNT - IT - MATE$ $\qquad$ T = _____

$BV = 2B(V + 1)$ $\qquad$ V = _____

$$\underset{-3}{\_\_}\ \underset{1}{\_\_}\ \underset{-4}{\_\_}\ \underset{-7}{\_\_}\ \underset{-8}{\_\_}\ \underset{7}{\_\_}\ \underset{-7}{\_\_} \qquad \underset{2}{\_\_}\ \underset{-1}{\_\_}\ \underset{-8}{\_\_}\ \underset{-3}{\_\_}\ \underset{3}{\_\_}\ \overset{W}{\underset{-4}{\_\_}} \qquad \underset{-8}{\_\_}\ \underset{-5}{\_\_}\ \underset{-1}{\_\_}$$

$$\underset{1}{\_\_}\ \underset{7}{\_\_}\ \underset{-1}{\_\_}\ \underset{-2}{\_\_}\ \underset{1}{\_\_}\ \underset{-7}{\_\_}\ \overset{L}{\underset{-8}{\_\_}}\ \overset{Y}{\underset{6}{\_\_}} \qquad \underset{2}{\_\_}\ \underset{3}{\_\_}\ \underset{-5}{\_\_}\ \underset{-1}{\_\_}$$

$$\underset{-2}{\_\_}\ \underset{-1}{\_\_}\ \underset{-5}{\_\_}\ \underset{-3}{\_\_}\ \underset{-8}{\_\_}\ \underset{7}{\_\_}\ \underset{-7}{\_\_}\ .$$

MATCHSTICKS

HERE ARE FOUR MATCHSTICK EQUATIONS WHICH ARE ALL FALSE AS THEY STAND. EACH ONE MAY BE MADE TO BE CORRECT BY CHANGING THE POSITION OF ONE AND ONLY ONE MATCHSTICK.

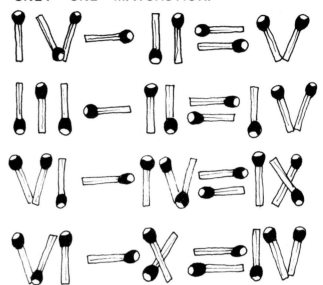

ADD FIVE MORE MATCHES TO THE SIX SHOWN BELOW TO MAKE <u>NINE</u> ONLY.

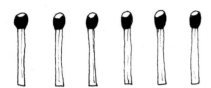

THE FOLLOWING EQUATIONS MAY BE CORRECTED BY MOVING TWO AND ONLY TWO MATCH STICKS.

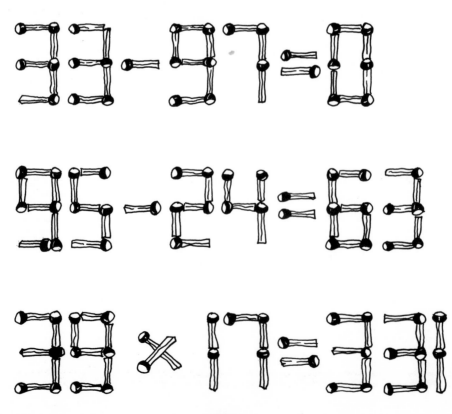

50

$$\overline{}_{-6} \quad \overline{}_{-6} \, \overline{}_{-5} \quad \overline{}_{4} \quad \overline{}_{6} \, \overline{}_{5} \, \overline{}_{1} \quad \overline{}_{6} \, \overline{}_{-7} \quad \overline{}_{-4} \, \overline{}_{-6} \, \overline{}_{1} \, \overline{}_{6} \, \overline{}_{4} \, \overline{}_{6} \, \overline{}_{-1} \, \overline{}_{-2} \, \overline{}_{4} \, \overline{}_{-6}$$

```
___   ___ ___   ___   ___ ___ ___   ___ ___   ___ ___ ___ ___ ___ ___ ___ ___ ___
-6    -6  -5    4     6  5  1    6  -7    -4 -6  1  6  4  6  -1 -2  4  -6
```

```
___ ___   ___ ___ ___ ___ ___ ___ ___   ___   ___ ___ ___ ___ ___ ___ ___ ___ ___   ___ ___
6  5      -1 -2  4  4  -6 -5  7        -6 -5  4  -2  6  5  6  5  1      4  2
```

```
___ ___ ___ ___ ___ ___   ___ ___ ___ ___ ___ ___ ___ ___   ___ ___ ___   ___ ___ ___ ___ ___
-2 -5  3  -6  5  4    -2  0  0  -6 -3  4  6  2  5    -2  5  3    -2 -5 -1 -6  3
```

```
___ ___ ___ ___ ___ ___ ___ ___   ___ ___   ___ ___ ___   ___ ___ ___ ___ ___ ___ ___ .
-3  2  5  0  -4  6  -3  4    -6  4    -6 -6  5    5  -2  4  6  2  5  -7
```

SOLVE EACH OF THE FOLLOWING INEQUALITIES AND DETERMINE THE <u>GREATEST</u> OR <u>SMALLEST</u> INTEGER SOLUTION. REPLACE THE GIVEN INTEGER EVERYWHERE IT APPEARS ABOVE BY THE CORRESPONDING CAPITAL LETTER. SEVERAL BLANKS ARE WITHOUT NUMERICAL CLUES AND MUST BE FOUND BY CONTEXT. AFTER YOU USE THE NUMBER CLUES TO DISCOVER THE ALGEBRA ADAGE, PARAPHRASE THE PROVERB IN ITS MORE FAMILIAR FORM.

$A > 3(1 + A)$

$2(C + 7) > 2 - C$

$7(D - 2) + 5 \leqslant 3(2 + D)$

$5E + 4 < 3E - 6$

$-3(F - 3) - 2 \leqslant F + 3(F + 4)$

$3(3G - 2) > 4G - 3$

$2[4 - 3(4 - I)] > 2I + 5$

$(3 - L)(L + 3) < -(L + 1)(L + 2)$

$(M - 3)(M + 1) \geqslant (M - 1)(M + 1)$

$-4[3 - 3(N - 3)] < 3(N - 2) + 11$

$2 - 3\sigma > 7 - 7\sigma$

$(R - 6)(R + 6) > (R + 7)(R - 1)$

$3|S| < 22$

$T(T - 1) \leqslant (T - 2)(T + 2)$

ALPHAMETICS

```
   NO
   IF
  xON
  xIF
 EVEN
```

```
 THIS
 SURE
   IS
PRIME
```

```
E V E N
  O D D
P R I M E
```

ODD is odd, EVEN is even, and PRIME sure is prime in each case.

```
R E D
F O R
x x x
x x x x
x x x x
D A N G E R
```

A very odd DANGER

```
  I T
T O O K
T H E
H I N T
```

A prime HINT

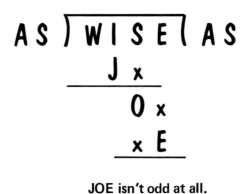

```
A S ) W I S E ( A S
    J x
    O x
    x E
```

JOE isn't odd at all.

SCRAMBLES

EACH OF THE FOLLOWING CONCERNS THE TOPIC OF EQUATIONS.

1. SO ROT

2. QUEEN TAL IV

3. NONCAUTION LID

4.† TONIE LOST US

5. COIL IT, DONNA

WORD REBUSES

1. MAN'S NAME + SAINT* + A LAUGH + NITROGEN*

   — — —   — — —   — — —   —

2. PREFIX FOR ACROSS + SIT FOR PAINTING

   — — — — — —   — — — —

3. CONCERNING + 101 (ROMAN) + IN FAVOR OF, FOR + GOLDEN STATE*

   — — —   — —   — — —   — — —

4. ACCEPTED BY THE GROUP + MATCH + ONE OF THE PLAYERS IN TAG + WHY

   — —   — — — —   — — — —   — —

5. PREFIX FOR EQUALLY + VET. ADMIN.* + SEASON FOR FASTING

   — — — —   — —   — — —

*Abbreviation
†Answer is two words.

53

Graphing

__ __ __ __ __ __ __ __ __ __ __ __ __ __ __ __ __ __
19 5 22 27 27 30   10 19 25 25 30 16 27 30 28 22 30 5

__ __ __ __ __ __ __ __ __ __ __ __ __ __ __ __ __ __
8 13 11 22 27 25 30 20   8 13 18   25 30 30 28 10   8 10

__ __ __ __ __ __ __ __ __ __ __ __ __ __ __ __
30 13 25 16 19 10   22 19 27 11 16   19 10   8 11 10

__ __ __ __ __ __ __ __ __ __ __ __ __ __ __ __ __ __ .
25 22 19 10 11   28 30 11 22 13 11   10 22 20 11 8 30 13

DETERMINE THE NUMBER OF THE EQUATION ON THE RIGHT WHOSE GRAPH IS
THE GIVEN LINE AND REPLACE THE NUMBER CLUE ABOVE BY THE CAPITAL
LETTER NAMING THE LINE. EACH OF THE UNCLUED BLANKS REPRESENTS A
DISTINCT LETTER. THE ALGEBRA ADAGE WILL DEVELOP AND MAY BE PARA-
PHRASED AS A COMMON PROVERB.

A has a slope of $-\frac{3}{4}$ and an x-intercept of six.

C has a slope of $\frac{4}{3}$ and passes through (6,4).

E passes through (−3,−4) and is parallel to 4x + 6y = 1.

F has slope $\frac{4}{3}$ and y-intercept six.

G is perpendicular to line passing through (3,−2) and (6,0), and has y-intercept of six.

I passes through the points (4,3) and (−2,12).

L has a slope of $-\frac{3}{2}$ and passes through the midpoint of segment from (5,−2) to (−1,8).

N passes through the points (0,6) and (9,0).

O passes through (3,−2) and is parallel to the line through (3,−4) and (6,−2).

P passes through $(-\frac{3}{2}, 2)$ and $(-2, \frac{4}{3})$.

R is parallel to 4x − 3y = 24 and passes through the point (3,−2).

S has x-intercept of −4½ and y-intercept of six.

T is perpendicular to 2x + 3y = 18 and has y-intercept of nine.

Y has a slope of $\frac{3}{2}$ and a y-intercept of nine.

1. 2x + 3y = 12
2. 3x − 4y = 18
3. 3x + 4y = −12
4. 3x + 2y = −18
5. 4x + 3y = 18
6. 3x + 4y = 12
7. 4x + 3y = −12
8. 3x + 2y = 18
9. 2x − 3y = −12
10. 4x − 3y = −18
11. 3x − 2y = 18
12. 3x − 2y = −12
13. 2x + 3y = 18
14. 3x − 4y = 12
15. 2x − 3y = −18
16. 3x − 2y = −18
17. 3x − 4y = −18
18. 3x + 2y = −12
19. 3x + 4y = 18
20. 4x − 3y = 12
21. 4x − 3y = 18
22. 2x + 3y = −18
23. 4x + 3y = −18
24. 3x + 4y = −18
25. 3x + 2y = 12
26. 2x + 3y = −12
27. 4x − 3y = 18
28. 4x − 3y = −12
29. 3x − 4y = −12
30. 2x − 3y = 12

CROSSNOMIAL PUZZLE

Each square contains exactly one sign, digit, or variable character. Thus the equation $y = 2x + 8$ may be entered as any one of the following. Notice the coefficient, if one, is not entered and equal signs are already inserted.

2	X	+	8	=	Y
8	+	2	X	=	Y
Y	−	2	X	=	8
−	2	X	+	Y	=	8

ACROSS

1. Line with slope 1 passing through the point (3,1/3).

8. Line with slope −1/2, passing through the point (−1/2, −2).

10. Line with slope 1/3 and intercept of (0, −67).

11. Line parallel to $6x + 5y = 1$ with y-intercept −6.

13. Line with intercepts (0,4) and (14,0).

14. Line perpendicular to $y = (1/17)x + 17$ with x-intercept 2.

15. _____ = 0 is a line through the points (1/4,4) and (1/2,24).

17. The x-intercept of $y = (1/5)x − 15$.

18. In the form $y = ax + b$, the slope is the coefficient of ____ .

19. See 16 DOWN.

DOWN

1. Line with slope 3/5 and y-intercept of −3.

2. _____ = 0 is line with slope −1/3 and x-intercept −36.

3. Line with slope 1/4 passing through the point (4,−5).

4. Line through (1,−2/3) and (5/6,−1).

5. Line perpendicular to 4 DOWN with y-intercept 10.

6. $y =$ _____ is a line through (−3,9) with y-intercept 90.

7. Line with y-intercept 8, passing through the point (1/6,−15).

8. Line passing through the points (14,3) and (−7,−3).

9. If $ax + by + c = 0$ is vertical, then $b =$ ___ .

12. If $y = mx + b$ and $m =$ ___, then the graph is a horizontal line.

16. See 19 ACROSS.

58

USE THE CLUES TO DISCOVER THE VALUES OF THE CAPITAL LETTERS. RE-
PLACE THE BLANKS BELOW BY THE CORRESPONDING LETTER, AND REWRITE
THE ALGEBRA ADAGE AS A COMMON PROVERB. (EACH OF THE TWO UNCLUED
BLANKS REPRESENTS A DISTINCT LETTER.)

$$\overline{}\ \overline{}\quad\overline{}\ \overline{}\quad\overline{}\ \overline{}\ \overline{}\qquad\overline{}\ \overline{}\ \overline{}\ \overline{}\ \overline{}\ \overline{}\ \overline{}\ \overline{}\ \overline{}\ \overline{}$$
7 9   −8 −3   8 12 −2   13 8 9 8 −2 6 7 −2 −5 9

$$\overline{}\ \overline{}\ \overline{}\quad\overline{}\ \overline{}\ \overline{}\ \overline{}\ \overline{}\qquad\overline{}\ \overline{}\ \overline{}\ \overline{}\ \overline{}\ \overline{}\ \overline{}\ \overline{}\ \overline{}\ \overline{}$$
−2 37 8   4 13 13 8 6   7 −2 2 −8 3 13 37 8 6 8

$$\overline{}\ \overline{}\ \overline{}\ \overline{}\quad\overline{}\ \overline{}\ \overline{}\ \overline{}\ \overline{}\ \overline{}\qquad\overline{}\ \overline{}\ \overline{}\ \overline{}\ \overline{}\ \overline{}\ \overline{}\ \overline{}$$
−5 6 6 8   −8 11 7 −3 29 −1   17 8 3 11 8 9 17 3 **.**

A is the Abscissa of (7,−3).

B is the ordinate of the point with abscissa two on y + 2x = 1.

C is the Constant such that (−3,1), (−1,6), and (1,C) lie on the same line.

D is the Distance between (−9,4) and (6,−4).

E is the slope of $\frac{1}{2}y = 4x + 8$.

H is the length of the Hypotenuse of the triangle with vertices (−17,−8), (18,4), and (18,−8).

I is the x-Intercept of the line with slope $-\frac{2}{3}$ and through (−8,2).

L is the Length of the segment of the line 21x + 20y = 210 between x = −10 and 10.

M is the x-coordinate of the Midpoint of the segment from (5,2) to (−1,6).

N is the Number of points on the graph of 3y = 2x + 9 on the interval $0 \leqslant x \leqslant 25$ with integer coordinates.

O is the Ordinate of the point on 4y + 7x = 3 whose abscissa is five.

P is the distance from the origin to the closest Point of: (5,12), (7,11), (10,9).

R is the "Rise" that will produce a "run" of 9 units on 3y = 2x + 15.

S is the Slope of the line perpendicular to x = −3y.

T is the x-coordinate of the midpoint of the longest side of the Triangle with vertices (−9,0), (5,4) and (3,0).

U is the number of Units below the origin 4x = 5y + 20 intersects the y-axis.

V is the Value of m in x = my + 2, if it passes through (−5,1).

Y is the Y-intercept of the line parallel to the line y = 3x + 5 and passing through the point (2,5).

CROSSWORD PUZZLE

THE CLUES DEAL WITH
THE TOPIC OF GRAPHING.

ACROSS

1. Near
3. (0,0)
9. Greyhound
11. Pairs
13. TL^{2}D
15. Marine Corps teacher
16. Either 1 DOWN or 3 DOWN
19. (x,y) is to __?__ as y = mx + b is to line
21. Observe beverage (2 words)
23. A point on 4x − 3y = 21 is (12, ?)
24. Brazil, Chile, Peru . . .
25. Prefix meaning "three"
27. (a,0) or (0,b)
30. x-intercept of 30 DOWN
31. Radio station
32. y-intercept of 30 DOWN
33. Insect
34. Level
35. Chiquita or Cabana
37. 3x + 4y = 7 and 6x + 8y = 9

DOWN

1. The first coordinate
2. To, too, two . . .
3. Vertical coordinate
4. Road (abbr.)
5. Permutation of IDEA
6. Sand, gravel
7. That is (abbr.)
8. Plains state
10. $-\frac{3}{4}$ in 37 ACROSS
11. __?__ but goodie
14. Jog
17. Negative suffix (contraction)
18. A long, long time
20. x = k : k ∈ Reals
22. Each
23. In the ___?___ of time
26. S.P., A.T.S.F., N.Y.C., etc.
28. Have same value
29. Two nonskew lines lie in the same __?__ .
30. (?, −2) lies in y = −2x + 8
32. Long skinny fish
33. Sheep talk
36. Giants, Dodgers, Mets, Reds . . .

PALATABLE PLOTTING

PLOT THE FOLLOWING POINTS ON A SINGLE SET OF COORDINATE AXES, CONNECTING THE POINTS WITH LINE SEGMENTS IN THE ORDER LISTED.

1.	(0,6)	6.	(14,11)	11.	(3,−4)	16.	(3,−7)
2.	(7,9)	7.	(17,10)	12.	(4,−7)	17.	(2,−4)
3.	(9,12)	8.	(14,9.5)	13.	(7,−8)	18.	(−2,−2)
4.	(11, 12.5)	9.	(11,1)	14.	(4,−7.5)	19.	(−9,−5)
5.	(13,12)	10.	(5,−2)	15.	(1,−8)	20.	(0,6)

Now the point (12.5,10.5) should complete the figure.

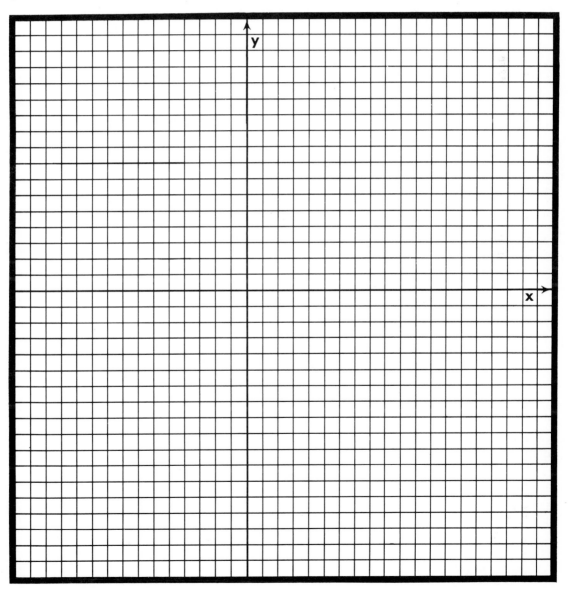

61

PALATABLE PLOTTING

COMPLETE THE FOLLOWING ON THE SAME SET OF COORDINATE AXES.

I   PLOT THE FOLLOWING TEN POINTS, CONNECTING THE POINTS WITH LINE SEGMENTS IN THE ORDER LISTED, TO FORM A CLOSED FIGURE.

1.	(–8,8)	5.	(10,4)	9.	(–12,4)
2.	(–3,10)	6.	(11,–3)	10.	(–8,8)
3.	(1,10)	7.	(–1,–9)		
4.	(6,8)	8.	(–13,–3)		

II   NOW CONNECT (–1,–9) TO EACH OF THE OTHER POINTS IN SET I WITH LINE SEGMENTS.

III   PLOT THE FOLLOWING IN ORDER, CONNECTING THE POINTS WITH LINE SEGMENTS.

1.	(5,–6)	3.	(–4,–10)
2.	(2,–10)	4.	(–7,–6)

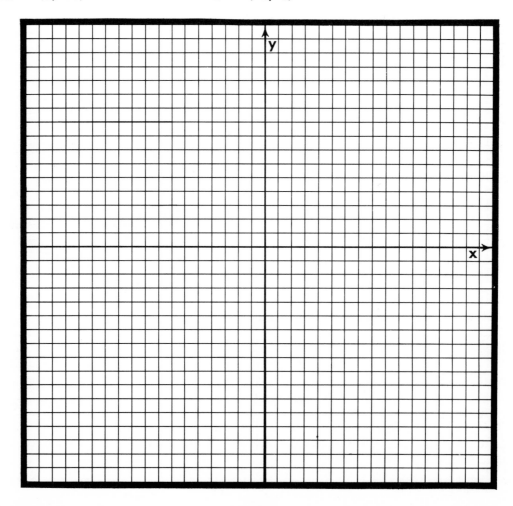

62

PALATABLE PLOTTING

SKETCH EACH OF THE FOLLOWING ON THE SAME SET OF COORDINATE AXES.
SET UP THE AXES SO THAT $-15 \leqslant x \leqslant 15$ AND $-15 \leqslant y \leqslant 25$.

1. $y + 6 = \dfrac{12}{7}(x + 4)$ $\quad:\quad$ $-6 \leqslant y \leqslant 6$

2. $y = 2$ $\quad:\quad$ $-12 \leqslant x \leqslant -7$

3. $y = x + 3$ $\quad:\quad$ $-4 \leqslant x \leqslant 12$

4. $y = x + 9$ $\quad:\quad$ $-7 \leqslant x \leqslant 9$

5. $y = -3$ $\quad:\quad$ $-15 \leqslant x \leqslant -10$

6. $y + 8 = \dfrac{12}{5}(x + 7)$ $\quad:\quad$ $-8 \leqslant y \leqslant -2$

7. $x = -9$ $\quad:\quad$ $-9 \leqslant y \leqslant -4$

8. $y = \dfrac{1}{2}x + \dfrac{9}{2}$ $\quad:\quad$ $-15 \leqslant x \leqslant -11$

9. $2y = 3$ $\quad:\quad$ $-8 \leqslant x \leqslant -6.5$

10. $4y - x = 63$ $\quad:\quad$ $9 \leqslant x \leqslant 13$

11. $x + 4 = 0$ $\quad:\quad$ $-6 \leqslant y \leqslant -1$

12. $y + 9 = 2(x + 9)$ $\quad:\quad$ $-9 \leqslant y \leqslant -5$

13. $y = 4x - 33$ $\quad:\quad$ $15 \leqslant y \leqslant 19$

14. $y = \dfrac{7}{12}x + 9$ $\quad:\quad$ $2 \leqslant y \leqslant 9$

15. $2x + 9 = 0$ $\quad:\quad$ $-2 \leqslant y \leqslant -0.5$

16. $y = \dfrac{3}{2}x + 12$ $\quad:\quad$ $-12 \leqslant x \leqslant -10$

17. $y = -1$ $\quad:\quad$ $-14 \leqslant x \leqslant -11$

18. $5x - 12y = -58$ $\quad:\quad$ $-14 \leqslant x \leqslant -8$

19. $y = \dfrac{2}{3}(x + 3)$ $\quad:\quad$ $-6 \leqslant y \leqslant -4$

20. $x = -7$ $\quad:\quad$ $-8 \leqslant y \leqslant -5$

21. $y = -(x + 5)$ $\quad:\quad$ $-1 \leqslant y \leqslant 2$

22. $y - 18 = -(x - 9)$ $\quad:\quad$ $15 \leqslant y \leqslant 18$

23. $2y - 3 = -2(x + 8)$ $\quad:\quad$ $-2 \leqslant y \leqslant 1.5$

24. $y - 3 = x + 3$ $\quad:\quad$ $-2 \leqslant y \leqslant 7.5$

From a design by Wally Box, 10/73.

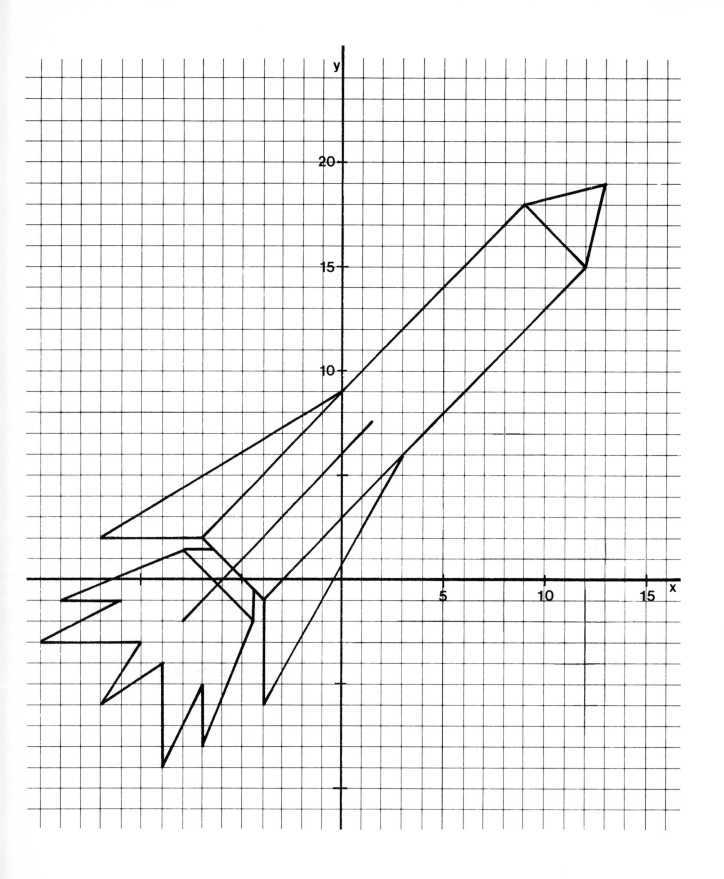

ALGEBRA SEARCH

This rectangular array of letters contains <u>at least</u> fifty words which may be arranged vertically, horizontally, or diagonally, and may be spelled frontwards or backwards. Only mathematical terms count and especially those relating to graphs and graphing. No duplicates!

```
S E P A R A L L E L T E R M O R E Z
P G N A X I S C P W N V S U B S E T
A D D E S O L C O A F I V E L H Q A
C E S N O I T U L O S O T N I O P Y
E C N E D N O P S E R R O C Q R L R
G N E T W P E I G H T D C L U I A A
R U O F A D O M A I N E I I E Z C D
A L R I S E E Q U A D R A N T O I N
P E R P E N D I C U L A R E A N T U
H S I N T E R C E P T N E V E T R O
N P A R A B O L A S S I C S B A E B
Z W N I G I R O R D I N A T E L V S
E E R H T G E C A R T E S I A N Y T
```

ALL TERMS DEAL WITH GRAPHING.

SCRAMBLES

1. NICEST DAY
2. ZOO INTHRALS
3. CANDY SITE
4. EAT IN ROD
5. D CAN EXIST
6. S AS BASIC
7. TUNIS
8. I CREPT TEN
9. SAND QUART
10. NO ACTOR DIES

65

Systems

Chapter Preview - Systems

ALGEBRA ADAGE

$\overline{}$ $\overline{}$ $\overline{}$ $\overline{}$ $\overline{}$ $\overline{}$ $\quad$ $\overline{}$ $\overline{}$ $\quad$ $\overline{}$ $\overline{}$ $\overline{}$ $\overline{}$ $\overline{}$ $\quad$ $\overline{}$ $\overline{}$ $\overline{}$ $\overline{}$ $\overline{}$ $\overline{}$ $\overline{}$ $\overline{}$

31 6 8 0 8 11   25 20   11 8 25 11 8   3 8 1 7 25 3 9 25 5

7 31 31 8 25 31 9 20 25   2   14 20 97 3   11 4 0 8 8 4 6 8 11

20 53 8 0   11   9 14 14 8 3   19 6 9 31 8   14 9   97 9 3

3 8 0 9 53 8 3   0 20 1   31 6 8   14 7 4 31 9 4

5 14 7 25 3 11   20   7   8 1 7 14 8   2 20 53 9 25 8 .

SOLVE THE FOLLOWING SYSTEMS OF EQUATIONS FOR CLUES TO COMPLETING THE PHRASE ABOVE.

1. $a + b = 9$ $a =$

    $a - b = 5$ $b =$

2. $2c + d = 11$ $c =$

    $3c - 2d = 6$ $d =$

3. $\frac{1}{2}e + 2g = 14$ $e =$

    $\frac{1}{4}e - 3g = -13$ $g =$

4. $\dfrac{18}{h} + \dfrac{27}{i} = 6$ $h =$

    $\dfrac{4}{h} + \dfrac{21}{i} = 3$ $i =$

5. $3L + 2m = 44$ $L =$

    $L = 4m + 10$ $m =$

6. $.4n + .1o = 12$ $n =$

    $.2n - .3o = -1$ $o =$

7. $9r + 2s - (s - r) = 11(r + 1)$ $r =$

    $4r - (r - s) = 5r + 11$ $s =$

8.   The average of two numbers is 64. Their difference is 66. What are the numbers?
(t = smaller number) $t =$
(u = larger number) $u =$

9.   Mrs. Smith spent $1.97 for three dozen eggs and two quarts of milk. Mrs. Jones spent $1.63 for two dozen eggs and three quarts of milk. What was the cost of a dozen eggs? of a quart of milk?
(v = cost of a dozen eggs) $v =$
(w = cost of a quart of milk) $w =$

NOW SEE IF YOU CAN SHORTEN THIS INTO A WELL-KNOWN FAMILIAR PHRASE.

UDDER NONSENSE!

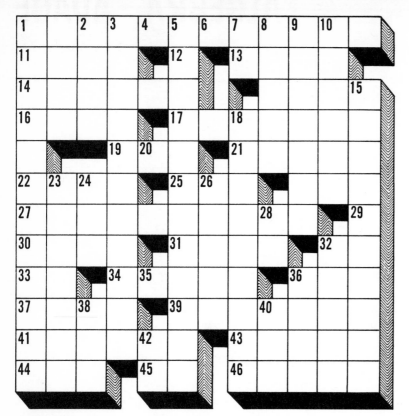

CROSSWORD PUZZLE

BE VERY SYSTEMATIC WITH THIS ONE!

ACROSS

1. The system: $\begin{cases} \text{14 ACROSS} - 4n = 0 \\ 6m - 8n = 1 \end{cases}$

   is ___?___
11. High ___?___
12. See 6 DOWN
13. If $\begin{cases} x - y = 0 \\ 2x - y = 9 \end{cases}$ then x = ?
14. See 1 ACROSS
16. Ht. (abbr.)
17. Bear, suffer, endure
19. Each, every
21. Permutation of HEREN
22. Very (German)
25. Apex, acme, zenith
27. The components of 1 ACROSS are not ___?___
29. See 12 ACROSS
30. Fidel's home
31. See 13 ACROSS, y = ?
32. Stormtroopers (abbr.)
33. Tantalum
34. Mixture
36. Bunch of holes sewn together
37. Italian (abbr.)
39. If $\begin{cases} 2x + 3 = y \\ 3y = 10x + 5 \end{cases}$ (coordinates of solution)
41. All vowels
43. See 36 DOWN
44. Northern Railroad (abbr.)
45. Like

DOWN

1. A point, if system is consistent
2. Heart
3. A horizontal line in the plane is the graph of a first degree equation in ___ _____ .
4. Nitrogen
5. ___?___ solution of a system
6. See 29 ACROSS
7. Tin
8. Man with stopwatch
9. Beseech, implore
10. $\begin{cases} \text{43 ACROSS} - 2m = 1 \\ \text{10 DOWN} - m = 4 \end{cases}$ such that (1, 4) is a solution
15. System with exactly one solution
18. System with infinitely many solutions
20. See 35 DOWN
23. Zero latitude
24. Center
26. Permutation of NILON
28. A compass point
32. See 39 ACROSS, 2x + y = ?
35. See 20 DOWN
36. $\begin{cases} \text{43 ACROSS} + m = 0 \\ 2n + m = 7, m = ? \end{cases}$
38. Atmosphere
40. A tree
42. Junior college degree

70

SOLVE EACH OF THE FOLLOWING FOR THE INDICATED VARIABLES AND USE THE VALUES TO DISCOVER THE ALGEBRA ADAGE AND THE PROVERB IT REPRESENTS.

$$\begin{cases} 7A + 11H = 35 \\ 6A - 12H = 30 \end{cases}$$

$$\begin{cases} 3E - 2V = 32 \\ \dfrac{E}{5} + 3V = -1 \end{cases}$$

If it is possible to change a $10 bill into an equal number of nickels, dimes, and quarters, then there are C coins of each type.

The side of one square is seven feet longer than the side of another square. The sides are T and U and the sum of perimeters of the squares is sixty feet.

The x-coordinate of the intersection of the lines $2y + 3x = 6$ and $5y + 3x = 6$ is L.

$$\begin{cases} o - 2g = 7 \\ \dfrac{5o}{4} - g = 8 \end{cases}$$

$$\begin{cases} 11M - 6Y = 10 \\ 9M - 5Y = 7 \end{cases}$$

Two trains leave a station going in opposite directions. After eight hours they are 360 miles apart. The Northbound train (N) is 3mph less than twice as fast as the Southbound train (S).

A total of $1200 is invested, part (I) at 3% and the rest (R) at 5%. Find the number of hundreds of dollars invested at each rate if the total interest is $54 for the year.

A Father is five times as old as his Daughter. In seven years he will only be three times as old. Find their present ages F and D.

A = _____
C = _____
D = _____
E = _____
F = _____
G = _____
H = _____
I = _____
L = _____
M = _____
N = _____
O = _____
R = _____
S = _____
T = _____
U = _____
V = _____
Y = _____

$\overline{3}\ \overline{29}\ \overline{7}\ \overline{3}\ \overline{-1}\ \overline{3}\quad \overline{7}\ \overline{4}\ \overline{5}\quad \overline{2}\ \overline{16}\quad \overline{25}\ \overline{6}\ \overline{29}\ \overline{11}\ \overline{3}\ \overline{29}\ \overline{4}\ \overline{3}\ \overline{29}\ \overline{-.5}$

$\overline{7}\ \overline{5}\ \overline{3}\ \overline{2}\ \overline{13}\quad \overline{35}\ \overline{4}\ \overline{29}\ \overline{25}\ \overline{11}\ \overline{3}\ \overline{6}\ \overline{29}\ \overline{16}\quad \overline{3}\ \overline{29}$

$\overline{16}\ \overline{11}\ \overline{9}\ \overline{4}\ \overline{25}\ \overline{11}\ \overline{4}\ \overline{9}\ \overline{10}\ \overline{16}\quad \overline{8}\ \overline{5}\ \overline{7}\ \overline{10}\quad \overline{6}\ \overline{35}\quad \overline{35}\ \overline{4}\ \overline{16}\ \overline{10}\ \overline{7}$

$\overline{16}\ \overline{5}\ \overline{29}\ \overline{7}\quad \overline{5}\ \overline{9}\ \overline{10}\quad \overline{29}\ \overline{6}\ \overline{11}\quad \overline{5}\ \overline{2}\ \overline{2}\ \overline{6}\quad \overset{W}{\overline{10}}\ \overline{7}\quad \overline{11}\ \overline{6}$

$\overline{0}\ \overline{4}\ \overline{9}\ \overline{2}\quad \overline{8}\ \overline{3}\ \overline{16}\ \overline{16}\ \overline{3}\ \overline{2}\ \overline{10}\ \overline{16}.$

MATCHSTICKS

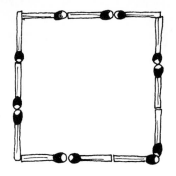
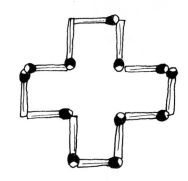

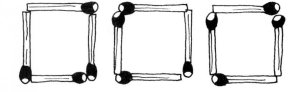

TAKE AWAY THREE OF THESE TWELVE MATCHSTICKS AND LEAVE TEN ONLY.

TWELVE MATCHSTICKS HAVE BEEN USED ABOVE TO FORM POLYGONS WITH AREAS OF NINE AND FIVE SQUARE UNITS. IF THE LENGTH OF EACH MATCHSTICK IS TAKEN AS ONE UNIT, FIND TWO OTHER POLYGONS FORMED WITH THESE MATCHES WITH AREAS OF EXACTLY SIX AND FOUR SQUARE UNITS.

REARRANGE THESE EIGHT MATCH-STICKS SO THAT YOU HAVE THREE SQUARES OF IDENTICAL SIZE.

HERE ARE A COUPLE OF

ALPHAMETICS

WHERE THE SPELLING IS BETTER THAN THE ARITHMETIC.

```
  SEVEN
  SEVEN
  SEVEN
+  NINE
-------
 TWENTY
```

```
    TWO
x   TWO
-------
  THREE
```

```
  EIGHT
- FIVE
-------
   FOUR
```

SOLVE EACH OF THE FOLLOWING SYSTEMS AND REPLACE THE VALUES BY THE CORRESPONDING LETTER.

$$\begin{cases} 5A - 2B = 17 \\ 8A + 5B = 19 \end{cases}$$

$$\begin{cases} 4I + 6 = 3H \\ 5H = 6I + 8 \end{cases}$$

$$\begin{cases} 3E - 8D - 13 = 0 \\ 2E = 11 + 3D \end{cases}$$

$$\begin{cases} 2L + 2N - 3\emptyset = -4 \\ 3L - 3N - 8\emptyset = 10 \\ 2L + 5N + 2\emptyset = 1 \end{cases}$$

$\emptyset$H N$\emptyset$!

A = _____

B = _____

D = _____

E = _____

H = _____

I = _____

G
$\underset{5}{\_}\ \underset{-3}{\_}\ \underset{-1}{\_}\ \underset{9}{\_}\ \underset{-3}{\_}\ \underset{-5}{\_}\quad \underset{5}{\_}\qquad \underset{5}{\_}\ \underset{-2}{\_}\ \underset{4}{\_}\ \underset{6}{\_}\ \underset{9}{\_}\ \underset{1}{\_}\qquad \underset{-1}{\_}\ \underset{7}{\_}$

V   Y
$\underset{7}{\_}\ \underset{-5}{\_}\ \underset{1}{\_}\ \underset{4}{\_}\ \underset{10}{\_}\ \underset{7}{\_}\ \underset{1}{\_}\qquad \underset{10}{\_}\ \underset{-3}{\_}\ \underset{2}{\_}\ \underset{-2}{\_}\qquad \underset{-3}{\_}\ \underset{5}{\_}\ \underset{-3}{\_}\ \underset{-1}{\_}\ \underset{-3}{\_}\ \underset{9}{\_}\ \underset{-3}{\_}\ \underset{2}{\_}$

R   F   C
$\underset{-1}{\_}\ \underset{6}{\_}\ \underset{2}{\_}\qquad \underset{-5}{\_}\ \underset{4}{\_}\ \underset{2}{\_}\qquad \underset{4}{\_}\ \underset{3}{\_}\ \underset{9}{\_}\qquad \underset{3}{\_}\ \underset{-3}{\_}\ \underset{9}{\_}\ \underset{-3}{\_}\ \underset{2}{\_}\ \underset{-3}{\_}\ \underset{7}{\_}\ \underset{5}{\_}\ .$

$$\begin{cases} \dfrac{2U}{3} + \dfrac{W}{5} = 6 \\[2mm] \dfrac{U}{6} - \dfrac{W}{2} = -4 \end{cases}$$

$$\begin{cases} \dfrac{2S - 1}{3} + \dfrac{T + 2}{4} = 4 \\[2mm] \dfrac{S + 3}{2} - \dfrac{S - T}{3} = 3 \end{cases}$$

L = _____

N = _____

$\emptyset$ = _____

S = _____

T = _____

U = _____

W = _____

CENTER x AND y AXES ON GRAPH PAPER.

1. $x + y = -4$

   $x - y = 2$

2. $x + y = -12$

   $2x + 3y = -26$

3. $2x + 3y = -17$

   $-2x - 6y = 14$

4. $.5x + .4y = -1.7$

   $1.2x + 8y = 10$

5. $x + \frac{1}{2}y = 0$

   $3x = 3 - 2y$

6. $x + 3y = 29$

   $2x - 5y = -41$

7. A certain coin collection consists of x dimes and y nickels. There are thirteen coins totaling $1.00. How many dimes and nickels are there?

8. The sum of two numbers is five. Their difference is thirteen. If x is the larger number and y is the smaller number, what are the two numbers?

9. $\dfrac{12}{x} - \dfrac{8}{y} = 7$

   $-\dfrac{4}{x} + \dfrac{12}{y} = -7$

10. $3y + 2x = 14$

    $x = 2y - 7$

OOPS!! ALMOST FORGOT THE FINAL DETAILS.

Draw a circle with center at (−2,3) and radius one.

Draw a circle with center at (−2,3) and radius one-half, and its interior.

Graph the solution set of the following system:

$$\begin{cases} x - 5y > -15 \\ 7x - 10y + 70 < 0 \\ x > -10 \end{cases}$$

(Solution on next page.)

PALATABLE PLOTTING

GRAPH THE FOLLOWING SYSTEMS OF INEQUALITIES ON THE SAME COORDINATE AXES.
SET-UP THE AXES SO THAT $-10 \leqslant x \leqslant 10$ AND $-15 \leqslant y \leqslant 15$.

1. $\begin{cases} -1 \leqslant x \leqslant 3 \\ -10 \leqslant y \leqslant -6 \end{cases}$

2. $\begin{cases} -6 \leqslant x \leqslant -2 \\ 4 \leqslant y \leqslant 8 \end{cases}$

3. $\begin{cases} -1 \leqslant x \leqslant 3 \\ y \leqslant x + 1 \\ y \geqslant -4 \end{cases}$

4. $\begin{cases} 8 \leqslant y \leqslant 12 \\ y \leqslant x + 14 \\ x \leqslant 3 \end{cases}$

5. $\begin{cases} y \leqslant -x + 14 \\ y \geqslant x - 4 \\ 3 \leqslant x \leqslant 7 \end{cases}$

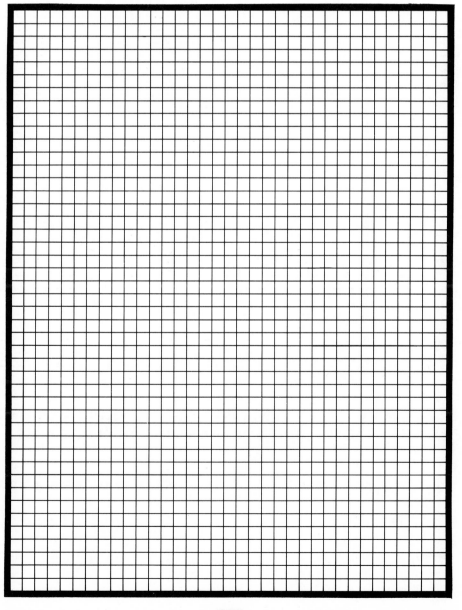

PALATABLE PLOTTING

GRAPH ALL THE SYSTEMS OF EQUATIONS AND INEQUALITIES ON THE SAME COORDINATE AXES.
SET UP THE AXES SO THAT $-20 \leqslant x \leqslant 10$ AND $-25 \leqslant y \leqslant 15$.

1. $\begin{cases} y = x + 12 \\ -14 \leqslant x \leqslant -5 \end{cases}$

2. $\begin{cases} y = x - 6 \\ -5 \leqslant x \leqslant 4 \end{cases}$

3. $\begin{cases} y < -x - 6 \\ -7 \leqslant x \leqslant -5 \\ y \geqslant -7 \end{cases}$

4. $\begin{cases} y \geqslant -x - 6 \\ -1 \leqslant y \leqslant 1 \\ x \leqslant -3 \end{cases}$

5. $\begin{cases} y = -x - 16 \\ -11 \leqslant y \leqslant -2 \end{cases}$

6. $\begin{cases} y = 2 - x \\ -2 \leqslant y \leqslant 7 \end{cases}$

7. $\begin{cases} y \leqslant x - 6 \\ -10 \leqslant 2x \leqslant -7 \end{cases}$

8. $\begin{cases} y \leqslant -x - 16 \\ -13 \leqslant 2x \leqslant -10 \end{cases}$

9. $\begin{cases} y \geqslant \frac{2}{3}x \\ x \geqslant -3 \\ y \leqslant -\frac{2}{3}x \end{cases}$

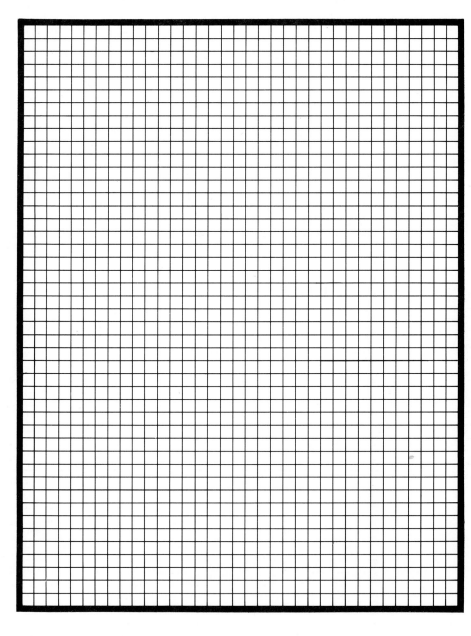

(ALTERNATE FORM) SET UP AXES SO THAT $|y + 5| \leqslant 20$ AND $|x + 5| \leqslant 15$ AND
GRAPH EACH OF THE FOLLOWING ON THE SAME COORDINATE AXES.

1. $|x + 6| \leqslant 1$ and $|y + 3| \leqslant 4$

2. $|3y| \geqslant 2x \; : \; x \geqslant -3$

3. $y + 11 \leqslant |x + 5| \; : \; |x + 5| \leqslant \frac{3}{2}$

4. $|x + 5| + |y + 2| = 9$

5. $|x + 4| \leqslant 1$ and $|y| \leqslant 1$

6. $y = -20 \; : \; 2|x + 5| > 3$

76

SCRAMBLES

FIND THE MATHEMATICAL TERMS WHOSE LETTERS HAVE BEEN REARRANGED. THESE DEAL WITH SYSTEMS.

1. SOUL MATE IN U.S.

2. C ISN'T STONE

3. TONIC IN TREES

4. I NEEDN'T PEND

5. SIN TINTS CONE

I REBUSE to talk to you!!

THESE WORD REBUSES

DEAL WITH SYSTEMS OF EQUATIONS. REMEMBER EACH CLUE SUGGESTS A WORD OR SYLLABLE OF A MATH TERM.

6. INSOLENT TALK − (PHOSPHORUS*) + CLOSE BY

__ __(__) __ __ __ __

7. INCORPORATED* + NOT OFF + FEMALE SIBLING + X + TIME*

__ __ __ __ __ __ __ __ __ __ __ __ __

8. DEUTERIUM* + A VOWEL + WRITING IMPLEMENT + FENDER DAMAGE

__ __ __ __ __ __ __ __ __

9. PRISONERS + 3RD PERS. SING. PRES. INDIC. OF BE + PORTABLE SHELTER

__ __ __ __ __ __ __ __ __ __

10. REPLACEMENTS + TITANIUM* + TEACH − (ALTERNATIVE) + CHARGED ATOM

__ __ __ __ __ __ __ __(__ __) __ __ __

*Abbreviation

77

Factoring

Chapter Preview - Factoring

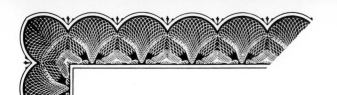

__ __ __ __ __ __ __ __   __ __ __ __ __ __ __   __ __
3y y y -y 187 9 3 7   11 17 0 7y 11 9 19   -3y 7y

__ __ __ __ __ __ __ __   __ __ __ __   __ __ __ __ __   __ __ __ __ .
-9 -3 -6 -9 4y 9 3 7   4y 3y -9 3   7y 7 -9 -y -y   -y 9 7y 7y

EACH CAPITAL LETTER HAS A DISTINCT VALUE. ALL VALUES CAN BE DETERMINED FROM THE CLUES BELOW. REPLACE THE BLANKS ABOVE BY THE CORRESPONDING LETTER AND DISCOVER THE ALGEBRA ADAGE. FINALLY, REPHRASE THE ALGEBRA ADAGE AS A COMMON PROVERB.

A must be Added to $y^2 + \dfrac{9}{4}$ to complete the square.

D is the coefficient of the second Degree term in $(2y - 3)(2 - 3y)$.

$(63)(57) = 60^2 - E$.

F is a Factor of $xy + yz + 2y$.

G is the Greatest "Common Monomial Factor" of $4y^3 + 8y^2 - 24y$.

I is an Integer such that the product of two more than I and three less than twice I is 147.

L is the Linear term of $(3y + 5)(4y - 7)$.

$x^2 + 2Nx + 9$ is a perfect Square.

O is the middle term of $(2y + 1)(2y - 1)$.

P is a Prime factor of the "Palindrome" 7337.

R is one of the solutions to $R^2 + 323 = 36R$.

$F + L + A + G = S$.

T is The coefficient of The linear Term in $(2y + 5)(3y - 4)$.

$(13 - 17)(13 + 11) = 13^2 + 13(-17 + 11) - U$

CROSSNUMBER PUZZLE

Factoring

ACROSS

1. One of the prime factors of this is number is 111.
6. The G.C.F. of 125, 350 and 625
7. $x^2 + 12x + ? = (\quad)^2$
8. A multiple of 3
9. The coefficient of the quadratic term in $[4(4x + 4)]^2$
11. The absolute value of the coefficient of the $x^2 y^2$ term resulting from $(4xy)^2 + (-5x)(-3xy)(-2y) = ?$
12. A perfect square which is divisible by 3 and 7 but has a remainder of 1 when divided by 2 and 5
14. 3 DOWN − [12 ACROSS + 17 DOWN + 6 ACROSS]
16. One more than the square of a cube
18. The solution of the following equation: $\dfrac{a^3 (a - 15)}{a^3} - (a^2)^0 = 0$, $a \neq 0$
20. $(x + ?)(x - 1) = x^2 + 98x - (?)$
21. $3(\quad)^2 (\quad)^2$ is divisible by 3, 9, 27 and the sixth prime number.

DOWN

1. $\sqrt{15876} = (?)$
2. The coefficient of the linear term in $\frac{1}{2}(x + 23)(x + 47)$
3. The constant term in $3(x - 15)(x - 17)$
4. $3x^2 + (?)x - 180 = (3x - 12)(x + 15)$
5. A perfect square
9. $2(\quad)^2 = 2x^2 + 44x + ?$
10. $2^4 \cdot 2^2 \cdot 2 \cdot 5 = ?$
13. $(x + 13)(x - 13) = x^2 - (?)$
15. 12 ACROSS + 4 DOWN
17. A prime number
18. The fourth power of a prime
19. The coefficient of the linear term in $(3x + 7)(6x + 7) = ?$

Remember the standard models for binomial factors!

$(a - b)(a + b) = a^2 - b^2$
$(a + b)^2 = a^2 + 2ab + b^2$
$(a - b)^2 = a^2 - 2ab + b^2$
$(a + b)(a + c) = a^2 + (b + c)a + bc$

All, of course, based on the distributive property:
$A[B + C] = AB + AC$

CROSSNOMIAL PUZZLE

Each square contains exactly one sign, digit, or variable character. Three plus signs (+) have been inserted because they occur at the end of a DOWN polynomial but are necessary to the ACROSS polynomial. Note that the terms of each polynomial may be permuted in many ways.

Find the missing factor or product in each problem.

ACROSS

1. $(?) (x - 1) = x^2 - 4x + 3$

4. $(2 + y) (?) = 2 - y - y^2$

7. $(?) (2x + y) = 2x^2 + 5xy + 2y^2$

8. $(x + 3) (?) = 63 + 18x - x^2$

10. $(-3) (?) = 6x + 3y + 6xy$

12. $2yz (?) = 6y^2z - 2yz + 8xyz + 2yz^2$

13. $(?) (xz) = xyz + x^2yz + xz^2$

14. $21 + y(4 + 3x) = ?$

17. $-3z(?) = 75xz - 6xyz^2$

18. $(?) (x + 3y) = x^2 - 9y^2$

19. $(3x - 2z) (?) = 12x^2 - 11xz + 2z^2$

20. $(?) (x + z) = x^2 + 2xz + z^2$

21. $(x - 3) (?) = x^2 + 2x - 15$

DOWN

1. $(?) (x - 2y) = x^2 - 4y^2$

2. $-3xz (?) = 6x^2z + 3xyz - 159xz$

3. $(?) (6xy) = 24x^2y^2z + 18xy^2 - 6xy$

4. $(-4) (y - 6x - 2) = ?$

5. $3x(z - 4) = ?$

6. $(9DOWN) (6DOWN) = xy^2z - x^2yz + (xyz)^2 - 5xyz$

7. $(2x + 5) (?) = 2x^2 - x - 15$

9. See 16DOWN

11. $(?) (x - 3) = y(x^2 - 2x - 3)$

14. $(5 - x) (?) = x^2 - 7x + 10$

15. $(?) (x + 11) = -(x^2 - x - 132)$

16. See 9DOWN

CROSSNUMBER PUZZLE

ACROSS

1. $x^2 + (?)x + 49 = (\quad)^2$
3. G.C.F. of 360, 108 and 252
5. $(84)(76) = 80^2 - (?)$
7. $(\quad)^2 = x^2 - 16x + (?)$
8. A multiple of four
9. $(4x + 3)(4x - 3) = (?)x^2 - 9$
10. Three of its prime factors are 29, 31 and 101
17. $\sqrt[3]{357,911} = (?)$
19. $(3 - 2)(3 + 10) = 9 + 3(-2 + 10) - (?)$
21. The coefficient of the linear term in $(2x + 5)^2$
22. The fourth power of a prime
24. $(x + 3)(x + 4) + (x - 3)(x - 4) = 2(x^2 + ?)$
26. An even square divisible by three
30. $(x + ?)(x - 1) = x^2 + 20x - ?$
32. 11 DOWN - 30 ACROSS + 25 DOWN
33. 32 ACROSS - 30 ACROSS

DOWN

1. $(x - 4)(x + 4) = x^2 - (?)$
2. $x^2 - 42x + (?) = (\quad)^2$
3. Has a remainder of one when divided by 3 or 5 or 11
4. $[5(x + 5)]^2 = 25x^2 + 250x + (?)$
5. The coefficient of x^2y^2 in $2y[(x^2 + 27y) (x^2 + 32y)]$
6. 1 ACROSS + 3 ACROSS + 5 ACROSS
11. $\sqrt{6889} = (?)$
12. Ten less than the constant term in $4[(x - 3)(x - 9)]$
13. The constant term in $(x + 7) (x + 11)$
16. $(\quad)^2 = 25x^2 + (?)x + 36$
18. The coefficient of the quadratic term in $(3x - 2)(6x + 5)$
21. Twice a prime
23. The coefficient of the linear term in $(x + 7)(x + 5)$
24. A perfect square
25. $(x - ?)(x - 1) = x^2 - 13x + (?)$
27. A prime number
28. $(x + ?)(x - 9) = x^2 + 5x - 126$
29. One of the solutions to the equation $x^2 - 7x = 78$

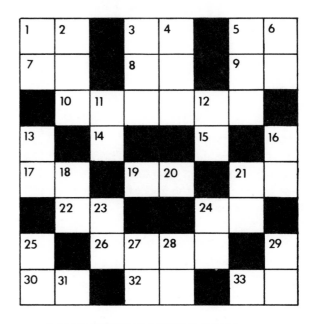

REMEMBER . . . . .
the standard models for binomial factors!!

$(a - b)(a + b) = a^2 - b^2$
$(a + b)^2 = a^2 + 2ab + b^2$
$(a - b)^2 = a^2 - 2ab + b^2$
$(a + b)(a + c) = a^2 + (b + c)a + bc$

All, of course, based on the distributive property:

$A[B + C] = AB + AC$

ALGEBRA ADAGE

$\dfrac{7}{3}$ -4 $\dfrac{2}{3}$ 3 $\dfrac{4}{3}$ $\dfrac{-5}{4}$ $\dfrac{1}{2}$ $\dfrac{3}{2}$ $\dfrac{1}{3}$ $\dfrac{-3}{4}$ $\dfrac{-5}{2}$ $\dfrac{2}{5}$ $\dfrac{-3}{4}$ -2 $\dfrac{4}{3}$ $\dfrac{-3}{4}$

$\dfrac{-1}{4}$ 3 0 $\dfrac{1}{2}$ $\dfrac{5}{4}$ -2 $\dfrac{5}{2}$ 2 ___ $\dfrac{3}{4}$ $\dfrac{4}{3}$ -3 $\dfrac{7}{3}$ 2 $\dfrac{3}{5}$ 0

$\dfrac{3}{2}$ $\dfrac{-3}{2}$ -5 $\dfrac{-5}{3}$ $\dfrac{3}{4}$ $\dfrac{5}{4}$ $\dfrac{-1}{2}$ $\dfrac{-1}{4}$ $\dfrac{-2}{3}$ $\dfrac{8}{5}$ 5 $\dfrac{1}{3}$ $\dfrac{5}{2}$ $\dfrac{1}{2}$ $\dfrac{-5}{4}$ $\dfrac{3}{5}$ $\dfrac{2}{3}$

$\dfrac{7}{3}$ 1 $\dfrac{8}{5}$ $\dfrac{-5}{3}$ $\dfrac{1}{2}$ $\dfrac{1}{5}$ $\dfrac{-3}{2}$ $\dfrac{-5}{4}$ $\dfrac{-2}{5}$ $\dfrac{2}{5}$ $\dfrac{1}{5}$ $\dfrac{1}{3}$ $\dfrac{4}{3}$ 2 $\dfrac{5}{2}$ -2 $\dfrac{-5}{3}$ $\dfrac{3}{4}$ $\dfrac{5}{4}$ $\dfrac{1}{2}$ $\dfrac{8}{5}$

$\dfrac{-3}{4}$ $\dfrac{-5}{2}$ $\dfrac{-2}{5}$ $\dfrac{2}{5}$ $\dfrac{-5}{4}$ $\dfrac{-4}{5}$ $\dfrac{1}{5}$ -4 -2 3 $\dfrac{3}{2}$ $\dfrac{-1}{4}$ $\dfrac{-1}{3}$

SOLVE THE QUADRATIC EQUATIONS AND REPLACE THE NUMBER CLUES ABOVE BY THE LETTERS USED AS VARIABLES IN THE EQUATIONS. EACH OF THE UNCLUED BLANKS REPRESENTS A DISTINCT LETTER. WHEN YOU HAVE DISCOVERED THE ALGEBRA ADAGE, PARAPHRASE IT AS A COMMON PROVERB.

1. $5A^2 = 6 - 7A$

2. $6C = C^2 + 8$

3. $13D - 4D^2 = -12$

4. $1 - 13E^2 + 36E^4 = 0$

5. $5I^2 - 11I = 12$

6. $K^2 - 15 = 2K$

7. $3(2L^2 - 6L + 3) = L - 1$

8. $20M^2 + M = 1$

9. $15N^3 = 14N^2 + 8N$

10. $10\cancel{0}^2 + 21\cancel{0} = 10$

11. $3(P^2 + 3P + 6) = 2(P^2 - 1)$

12. $8R^2 + 15 = 22R$

13. $15S^2 - 59S + 56 = 0$

14. $12T^2 + 35T + 25 = 0$

15. $8U^2 + 6U = 9$

16. $Y = 3Y^2 - 2$

ACROSS

1. $y = 5x + 16$
   $(20, \ ? \ )$
4. $2y + 4x = 198$
   $(-12, \ ? \ )$
7. $-3x + 2y = -47$
   $(\ ? \ , 11)$
8. The y-intercept of $2x + 3y = 39$
9. 20 more than 5 DOWN
10. Only one month has this many
11. $P_1 \ (-7, 45), P_2 \ (48, 48), m = \dfrac{\ }{?}$
13. $m = . \ \underline{?} \$ if $26x + 128y = 28$
15. A palindromic cube
18. See 35 DOWN
19. See 9 ACROSS
20. 4(8 ACROSS)
21. $m = \dfrac{266}{6} \ , 3y = \underline{\ ?\ } \ x + 150$
24. $-87x + 6y = 2; \ m = \dfrac{?}{66}$
27. A coordinate of the origin
28. The 25th triangular number
30. A multiple of 5
31. The y-intercept of a line with a slope of 1 and passing through $P(-21, 21)$
32. $m = \dfrac{?}{33}$ for a line perpendicular to $3x + 4y = 16$
33. $m = \underline{\ \ \ }\ \underline{\ \ \ }$ for $8y - 14x = 72$
34. 19 ACROSS – 18 DOWN

36. $\dfrac{3}{7}$ (15 ACROSS)
37. Product of 5th and 9th primes
39. A perfect square
40. A cube
41. Has factors of 2, 3, 6, and 9
42. The x-intercept of $\dfrac{1}{2}x + \dfrac{7}{8}y = 7$

DOWN

1. The x-intercept of $2x + 5y = 24$
2. The abscissa of $P(135, 137)$
3. $-x + 30y = 60; \ m = . \ \underline{?} \$ (in decimal notation)
4. Find the ordinate for $5x + y = 147$ when the abscissa is 0
5. See 7 ACROSS
6. $m = . \ \underline{?} \$ if the line passes through $P_1 \ (6, -12) \ P_2 \ (-6, -13)$
10. If $m = 5$ and the line passes through $P(1, 111)$ what is the ordinate when the abscissa is 19?
12. A prime
13. A multiple of 5 DOWN
14. A square number that is also a cube
16. The product of the x- and y-intercepts of the line $9x + 5y = 45$
17. The inverse of 7 ACROSS
18. 15 ACROSS – 310
22. The y-intercept of $5x + 6y + 15 = 15$
23. The abscissa of all y-intercepts
24. (11 ACROSS) (41 ACROSS)
25. A palindromic number
26. A square number squared
28. See 14 DOWN
29. $m = . \ \underline{?} \$ if the line passes through $P_1 \ (6, -1) \ P_2 \ (-14, -2)$
31. Permutation of a jumbo jet
32. Multiple of the slope of a line parallel to $-20x + 2y = 14$
33. $m = . \ \underline{?} \$ for $64y = 9x + 128$ (first three digits only)
34. Has factors of 3 and 37
35. See 18 ACROSS
36. A factor of 39 ACROSS
38. 28 DOWN – 3(34 ACROSS)

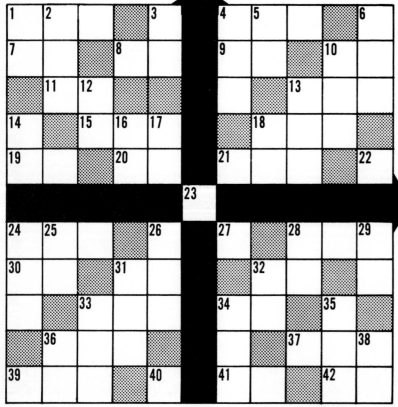

CROSSNUMBER PUZZLE

CROSSWORD PUZZLE

ACROSS

1. "Inverse" of out
5. Photos
8. 21 for 231, 273 & 147
11. $x^2 + 7x + 10 = 0$ is an ___?___
12. mc^2
13. Phone
14. π
15. 1005
16. Yell and scream
17. Watch intently
19. Diversion
21. $x = 2$ for $3x + 7 = 13$
23. Negative
24. HO^2
25. G.C.F. of:
    $6b^2e^2 - 15be^2 + 10b^2e$
26. $d = 2(?)$
27. 10 in 11 ACROSS
32. $a^2 \dfrac{om^3}{(am)^2} = ?$
33. $\dfrac{A}{L}$
34. $a + b$ is a ___?___
37. Also
39. One
40. Ten
41. Tuf
42. Every, abbr.
43. One solution of $x^2 + 15 = 8x$
44. $-8x$ is the ___?___ term in **43 ACROSS**

DOWN

1. $x^2 + 6x + 9$ is a ___?___
2. Gold
3. A ___?___ of $6x^2 - 19x + 15$ is $3x - 5$
4. η or H
5. $3x + 2$, $4x^2 - x + 1$ and $2x^3$ each is
   a ___?___
6. "Inverse" of out
7. $(x - 2)(x^2 + 5x) = x^3 + 3x^2 - 10(?)$
9. $3xy$ is a ___?___ factor of
   $9x^2y - 18xy^2 + 6x^2y^2$
10. One solution of $x^2 + 5x = 2x^2$
11. Corny
12. The sum of the solutions of
    $x^2 - 8x - 8 = 0$
14. $2L + 2W$
18. A long time
20. oa^2
25. Sheepish cry
27. "Inverse" of go
28. Senator
29. The product of the solutions of
    $x^2 + 2 = 0$
31. $\dfrac{102r^2}{17r} = ?$
35. G.C.F. of two primes
37. ___?___ 4 2
38. Rowing gear
39. That

87

1.

```
  E I G H T
  N I N E
  T H R E E
  ───────
  T W E N T Y
```

2.

```
        U N
        U N
      D E U X
    D O U Z E
    ─────────
    S E I Z E
```

3.

```
T W E N T Y
  F I V E
  F I V E
─────────
T H I R T Y
```

Go ahead, TRY is a perfect square.

4.

```
T H I R T Y
F O R T Y
    T E N
─────────
E I G H T Y
```

EIGHTY is divisible by 4, of course.

5.

```
T W E N T Y
T W E N T Y
T H I R T Y
T H I R T Y
─────────
H U N D R E D
```

But in this case TEN is a multiple of 19.

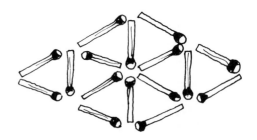

MATCHSTICKS

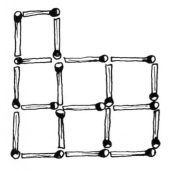

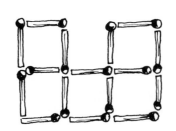

MOVE THREE SO THAT ONLY FIVE SQUARES REMAIN.

MOVE THREE SO THAT ONLY FOUR SQUARES REMAIN

REMOVE FOUR SO THAT ONLY FOUR TRIANGLES REMAIN.

SCRAMBLES

REARRANGING THESE IS GOING TO BE NO PICNIC! SOME ARE MATH PHRASES.

1.   CRAB OF LATE

2.   UP GRINGO

3.   FRIED FENCE

4.† DARN MAD FROST

5.† FREE SQUERT CAP

*Abbreviation

†Answer is two words.

6.   REALITY + CONJUNCTION + ADROIT

— — — —   — — —   — — — —

7.   DISAGREE + REPEAT PERFORMANCE − (NATIVE METAL) + EAST*

— — — — — — — — —(— — —) —

8.   FORCE* + DRAMATIC ARTIST + NOT BEYOND + UNIT OF GRAVITATIONAL FORCE*

— — — — — — — — — —

9.   THIS(BROOKLYNESE) + THREE(PREFACE) + HOWEVER + I HAVE

— — — — — — — — — — — — —

WORD REBUSES

AFTER THOSE EASY ABOVE, TRANSLATING THIS SHOULD BE NO TROUBLE AT ALL!! HEH, HEH!!

Y Y U R Y Y U B I C U R Y Y 4 M E

89

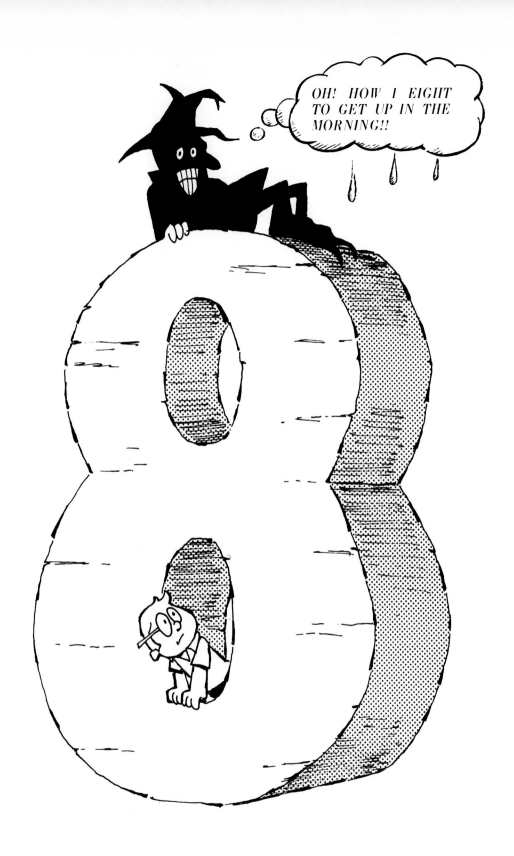

Fractions

Chapter Preview - Fractions

ALGEBRA ADAGE

DETERMINE THE VALUE OF THE CAPITAL LETTER IN EACH STATEMENT AND USE IT TO FILL IN THE PHRASE. THEN FIND THE PROVERB.

A = _____
B = _____
D = _____
E = _____
F = _____
H = _____
I = _____
L = _____
M = _____
N = _____
Ø = _____
P = _____
R = _____
S = _____
T = _____
U = _____
W = _____
Y = _____

$$\frac{18xy}{24xy} = \frac{A}{8y}$$

$$\frac{32x^3y^3}{64x^2y} = \frac{2x^2y^2}{D}$$

$$\frac{7xy}{14yz} = \frac{x}{F}$$

$$\frac{10xy}{5y^2 + 20y} = \frac{I}{y+4}$$

Puzzle blanks:

___ ___
2x 2z

___ ___ ___ ___ ___ ___ ___ ___ ___
3z 7y 2x 5y 6y 7y 2x −3 8x

___ ___ ___ ___ ___ ___ ___
2z 6y 2x −3 6x² 7y 7x

___ ___   ___ ___ ___ ___ ___ ___ ___ ___ ,
2x 60   2x 5y 5y 2x 4y 7x 4y 5x

___ ___ ___   ___ ___ ___ ___ ___ ___ ___ ___
4y 7x 3x   6y 5x 5x 7x 5y 3z 5x 60

___ ___ ___ ___ ___ ___   ___ ___   ___ ___ ___ ___
60 3y −2 6x² −3 4x   2y 7x   5y 6y 4x 7x

___ ___ ___ ___ ___ ___ ___ ___ ___ ___ ___ ___ ___ ,
7y 7x 3z 7x 5x 2x 5x 2x −2 6x² 60 −3 8x

$$\frac{2}{x} + \frac{3}{y} = \frac{B + 3x}{xy}$$

$$\frac{5x}{3} - \frac{9 - 2x}{3} = \frac{E - 9}{3}$$

$$\frac{4y}{3} + \frac{5y}{3} = H$$

$$\frac{8}{x} + \frac{2}{x} - \frac{3x + 10}{x} = L$$

$$\frac{(3x)^3}{y^2} \cdot \left(\frac{y}{2x}\right)^2 - \frac{3x}{4y}(5y) = W$$

The reciprocal of $\frac{3x}{15xy}$ is M.

$\frac{x-2}{x+2}$ is not defined for x = Ø

$$\frac{xy}{14} \div \frac{y^2}{6} = \frac{3x}{R}$$

$$\left(\frac{T}{6y}\right)\left(\frac{6xy}{5}\right) = x^2$$

$$\frac{\frac{y}{3} - \frac{y}{5}}{\frac{1}{2}} = \frac{N}{15}$$

$$\frac{8}{z^3} \div \frac{12}{z^2} = \frac{2}{P}$$

$$\frac{5y}{7} \cdot \frac{2x}{y} \div \frac{x^5}{42} = \frac{S}{x^4}$$

The least common multiple of x, 2x², 3, and 6x is U.

The greatest common factor of 24x², 32x³, and 56x is Y.

93

CROSSNOMIAL PUZZLE

Each square contains exactly one sign, digit, or variable character. Two plus signs (+) have been inserted because they occur at the end of a DOWN entry, but are necessary to the ACROSS entry. Notice that the terms of each factor may be permuted in several ways.

ACROSS

1. $\dfrac{x^2 - 3x + 2}{x^2 - 4x + 4} = \dfrac{x - 1}{?}$

4. $\dfrac{x^2 - 2x - 24}{x^2 - x - 20} = \dfrac{?}{x - 5}$

7. $\dfrac{1}{y} + \dfrac{3}{x} = \dfrac{?}{xy}$

8. $x + \dfrac{1}{y} = \dfrac{?}{y}$

10. $\dfrac{1}{5x} - \dfrac{1}{y} = \dfrac{?}{5xy}$

12. $(-2)^5$

13. See 20 DOWN

14. $\dfrac{\dfrac{1}{y} - \dfrac{z}{7}}{3x} = \dfrac{24 \text{ ACROSS}}{?}$

15. $\dfrac{6y - 6xyz}{-3y} = ?$

17. $\dfrac{x^2 - 6xz + 5z^2}{x^2 - z^2} = \dfrac{?}{27 \text{ ACROSS}}$

19. $\dfrac{1}{3y} + \dfrac{3}{x} = \dfrac{?}{3xy}$

22. $\dfrac{2y - x}{y + 3x}$ is undefined for $y = ?$

23. $\dfrac{1}{yz} + \dfrac{3}{x} = \dfrac{?}{21 \text{ DOWN}}$

24. See 14 ACROSS

26. See 1 DOWN

27. See 17 ACROSS

28. $\dfrac{?}{y - 7} = \dfrac{y^2 + 6y - 7}{y^2 - 8y + 7}$

DOWN

1. $-\dfrac{2x^2 + 9xy - 5y^2}{2x^2 - 7xy + 3y^2} = \dfrac{?}{26 \text{ ACROSS}}$

2. $\dfrac{?}{5xy - 9x} = \dfrac{3 + 25y}{9 - 5y}$

3. $\dfrac{?}{6xyz} = \dfrac{1}{3xz} + \dfrac{1}{2y}$

4. See 25 DOWN

5. $\dfrac{1}{4x} - \dfrac{1}{12y} - \dfrac{1}{xy} = \dfrac{?}{12xy}$

6. $\dfrac{1}{3} - \dfrac{3}{x + 2} = \dfrac{17 \text{ DOWN}}{?}$

7. $\dfrac{5x}{5x^2 - 20x} = \dfrac{1}{?}$

9. See 14 DOWN

11. See 25 DOWN

14. $\dfrac{24y - 12xy + 36y^2}{9 \text{ DOWN}} = ?$

16. See 25 DOWN   23. G.C.F. of xy, xyz, and xz.

17. See 6 DOWN

18. $\dfrac{6 + z - z^2}{z^2 - 9} = \dfrac{z + 2}{?}$ 25. $\dfrac{4 \text{ DOWN}}{25 \text{ DOWN}} = \dfrac{11 \text{ DOWN}}{16 \text{ DOWN}}$

20. $\dfrac{4y^2 + 5y - 6}{9y^2 + 11y - 14} = \dfrac{13 \text{ ACROSS}}{?}$

21. L.C.D. for $\dfrac{1}{xy} + \dfrac{1}{xz} - \dfrac{1}{yz}$.

94

$\underline{}$ $\underline{}$ $\underline{}$ $\underline{}$ $\underline{}$ $\underline{}$ $\underline{}$ $\underline{}$ $\underline{}$ $\underline{}$ $\underline{}$ $\underline{}$ $\underline{}$ $\underline{}$ $\underline{}$ $\underline{}$ $\underline{}$ $\underline{}$ $\underline{}$ $\underline{}$ $\underline{}$ $\underline{}$

5 7 25 1 Ø 5   –2 15 Ø –2 2 12 5 –5 15 –7   4 3 35 1   1 25

4 7 10   Ø 5 –5 15 12 4 –7   35 2   5 7 0 4 0 5   1 7

Ø 5 3 Ø 5 4 25 1 2 7   3 4 15 12 5 12   4   9 4 –7 5

4 10 2 –7 5 12 3 5 7 35   25 2   5 3 2 9 5   4

10 5 –2 Ø 5 12 12 5 10   1 10 .

SOLVE THE FOLLOWING EQUATIONS FOR CLUES TO THE ALGEBRA ADAGE ABOVE. NOTE THAT SEVERAL BLANKS ARE WITHOUT NUMERICAL CLUES AND MUST BE FOUND BY CONTEXT.

1. $\dfrac{2}{3} = \dfrac{a}{6}$ a =

2. $\dfrac{1}{2} = \dfrac{5}{c + 7}$ c =

3. $\dfrac{d}{2} - \dfrac{d}{5} = 3$ d =

4. $.4e + 5 = .6e + 4$ e =

5. $\dfrac{f + 1}{2} - \dfrac{f - 3}{4} = f + 5$ f =

6. $\dfrac{g + 5}{10} - \dfrac{g}{4} = \dfrac{2 + g}{4}$ g =

7. $\dfrac{3}{i} + \dfrac{8}{i} = 11$ i =

8. $-\dfrac{14}{L} - \dfrac{49}{L^2} = 1$ L =

9. $\dfrac{2}{m + 3} + \dfrac{m + 5}{m + 3} = \dfrac{-(2m - 2)}{-3 - m}$ m =

TRANSLATE THE ALGEBRA ADAGE INTO THE PROVERB IT PARAPHRASES.

10. $\dfrac{1}{n - 3} = \dfrac{3}{n + 5}$ n =

11. $\dfrac{o + 3}{o - 1} + \dfrac{o + 1}{o - 3} = 2$ o =

12. $\dfrac{4}{p - 1} + \dfrac{1}{p + 4} = \dfrac{5}{p^2 + 3p - 4}$ p =

13. $\dfrac{r + 3}{r^2 - 1} + \dfrac{r - 3}{r^2 - r} = \dfrac{2r}{r^2 + r}$ r =

14. A ribbon 21 inches long is divided into parts whose ratio is 3 : 4. Find the length of the longer piece.   s =

15. The sum of two numbers is 60. If $\dfrac{2}{7}$ of the larger number is added to $\dfrac{3}{5}$ of the smaller number, the sum is 25. Find the numbers.   t = or

16. A barge travels 36 miles down a river in the same amount of time it takes it to travel 24 miles back up. The current of the river is 3 miles per hour. What is the rate of the barge in still water?   u =

CROSSWORD PUZZLE

ACROSS

1. Lowest ___?___
6. 16% of 400 = ? (Rom. numeral)
10. The product of I and E
11. 50% of 2et is ?
13. $(ed)^2 \cdot \dfrac{a}{b} \cdot \dfrac{c}{d} \div \dfrac{ce^2}{b}$
14. L, M, ? , O, 1, 2, 3
15. 7% of $71.42\overline{85714285}$ is ?
17. A small part
18. Part of the base
21. M ___?___ phone
22. There are two in every denominator
23. 1 ACROSS ∩ 5 DOWN
24. Stone
26. A ___?___ of π
30. One hundred
31. Diminutive of Christina or Albertina
33. Reversed site
35. Inches and feet, as well as months and years, have the same ?
40. Necktie used for parties and special occasions
42. PRT
43. $\dfrac{(32\ DOWN)^2}{(22\ ACROSS)}$ = ?
44. 80% of 2500 lbs is ?
45. Divide out common factors in the numerator and denominator

DOWN

1. At what yearly rate of interest does $100 earn $5 in six months?
2. Area of the figure: $e\ \square_i$
5. $140 can be earned with $2,000 in one year, invested at a rate of how many %?
8. "Do you get it?"
9. V8
12. (?) : 16 = 7.5 : 12
15. 5 : 4 or 5 ÷ 4 or 1.25 or as a ?
16. An answer to 8 DOWN
17. Part is to whole as percentage is to ___?___
19. Self esteem
25. Tangent lips
26. Average
34. In addition
36. HELP!!
39. $\dfrac{1}{25}$ is 4% of what number?
41. Ah

96

FIND THE VALUES OF THE LETTERS IN THESE **ALPHAMETICS** FRACTIONS. THEIR ASSOCIATED DIVISIONS MAY HELP.

$$\frac{AN}{EASY} = \frac{1}{ONE}$$

```
        _____
  AN )  EASY ( ONE
       x T
       _____
       x x x
       x x R
       _____
         x x
         x Y
         _____
```

$$\frac{SEVEN}{TWO} = TWO$$

```
         _____
  TWO )  SEVEN ( TWO
         BOB
         _____
         JOE
         OVV
         _____
         VESN
         VESN
         _____
```

```
  FOR )  DANGER ( RED
         x x A x
         _____
         x D x x
         x D x x
         _____
           x x x
           x x x
           _____
```

$$\frac{FOR}{DANGER} = \frac{1}{RED}$$

```
  HIP )  HURRAY ( HIP
         x x x x
         _____
         x x x x
         x x H O
         _____
         x x x x
         R A A Y
         _____
```

$$(HIP)(HIP) = HURRAY$$

MATCHSTICKS

THESE EQUATIONS ARE ALL FALSE. YOU MAY MOVE ONLY ONE MATCH IN EACH EQUATION TO MAKE IT TRUE.

FIND TWO DISTINCT SOLUTIONS FOR NUMBERS ONE AND TWO. NUMBER THREE IS AN APPROXIMATION.

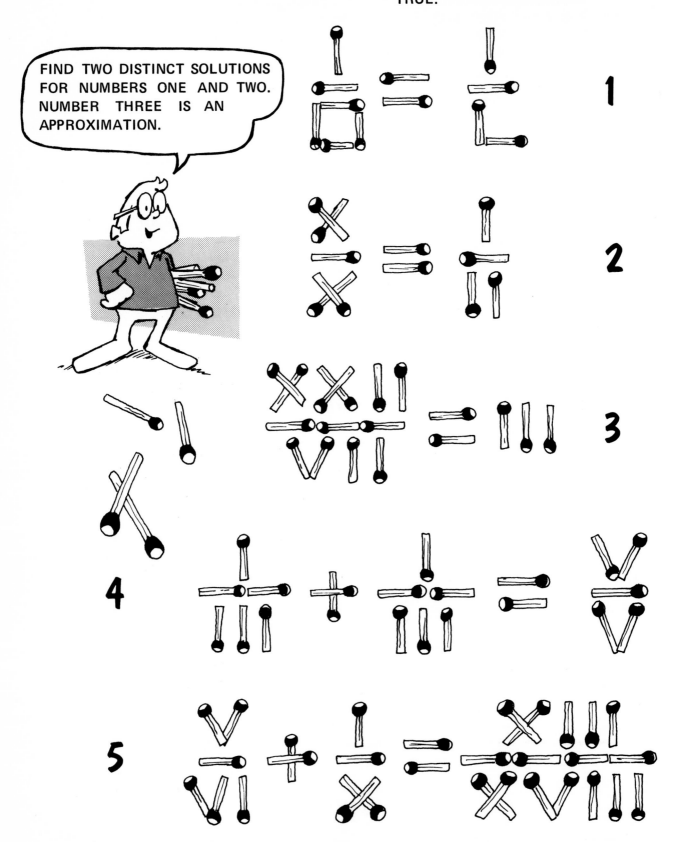

HERE ARE SOME **SCRAMBLES** DEALING WITH FRACTIONS. UNSCRAMBLE THE FIRST FIVE AND REMEMBER IN THE SECOND FIVE EACH CLUE SUGGESTS A WORD OR SYLLABLE.

1. MAD NINE ROOT

2. CLAP OR RICE

3. TENCE GRAPE

4. I GAB CLEAR

5. RUNG DICE

WORD REBUSES

6. EXPERT + LEFT SIDE + ME + TAKING PLACE

— — —   — — — —   — —   — —

7. FRANC* + PERFORM + PRONOUN + ATOP

— —   — — —   — —   — —

8. INFORMER + A COUPLE OF VOWELS

— — —   — —

9. LAIR + OXYGEN* + LEAST* + ON OR NEAR + CONJUNCTION

— — —   — —   — — —   — —   — —

10. EXAMPLE* + SQUEEZE + CHARGED ATOM

— —   — — — — —   — — —

*Abbreviation

Radicals

USE THE CLUES SUPPLIED CONCERNING RADICALS TO COMPLETE THE PHRASE. THEN DISCOVER THE ALGEBRA ADAGE DISGUISED THEREIN.

SHHH!

$$A = \sqrt{7^2 + 24^2}$$

$$\sqrt{C} \approx 5.291503$$

$$N = 7\sqrt{9} + 5\sqrt{4}$$

$$O = \frac{\sqrt{20} + 4\sqrt{5}}{\sqrt{10}}$$

$$Y = \sqrt{\frac{15}{2}} \ \sqrt{\frac{14}{5}} \ \sqrt{\frac{1}{7}} \ \sqrt{\frac{2}{3}}$$

$$I = \sqrt{300} - \sqrt{12} + \sqrt{48} - \sqrt{75} + \sqrt{147} - \sqrt{432}$$

$$\overline{32} \ \overline{25} \ \overline{28} \ \overline{2\sqrt{3}} \ \overline{32} \ \overline{12} \ \overline{40} \ \overline{31} \ \overline{2\sqrt{3}} \ \overline{32} \ \overline{\sqrt{2}} \qquad \overline{2\sqrt{3}} \ \overline{-2}$$

$$\overline{25} \ \overline{12} \ \overline{40} \ \overline{3\sqrt{2}} \ \overline{12} \ \overline{-2} \ .$$

$$T = \frac{1}{7}(2 + 3\sqrt{2})(3 - \sqrt{2})(2 + \sqrt{2})(\sqrt{2} - 1)(16)$$

$$R = \sqrt{41^2 - 9^2}$$

$$S = (1 - \sqrt{3})(2 + \sqrt{3})(\sqrt{3} - 1)$$

$$U \approx \sqrt{7} + \sqrt{11} + \sqrt{35}$$

CROSSNUMBER PUZZLE

<u>RADICALS</u>

ACROSS

1. $\sqrt{6889}$

3. $\sqrt{128} = ?\sqrt{2}$

4. $(3\sqrt{2} \cdot 23)^2$

7. $(\sqrt[3]{2})^3 (\sqrt[3]{5}) = \sqrt[3]{?}$

8. $\dfrac{5}{\sqrt{12}} = \dfrac{10\sqrt{3}}{?}$

10. $\sqrt{2304} = ?$

11. $2\sqrt{5}\sqrt{263} = \sqrt{?}$

13. The integer closest to $\sqrt{14.407}$ is ___?___ .

14. $\dfrac{1550}{3333} = \dfrac{}{.\ ?}$

16. The product of (24 ACROSS) and 3 more than (10 ACROSS)

18. The integer closest to $\sqrt{\dfrac{1}{81}}$

19. The constant term in
    $(x - 3)(x + 7)(x - 67)$

22. $(7 - \sqrt{17})(7 + \sqrt{17})$

24. Solve for x:
    $5x^2 - 3920 = 0,\ x > 0$

25. $\sqrt{9}\ \sqrt{169} = ?$

27. Find 31x where
    $x^2 - 22x = 0,\ x > 0$

29. $2(\sqrt[3]{64})(\sqrt{64}) + 5$

DOWN

1. 7 times (8 ACROSS)

2. The rationalized denominator of
    $\dfrac{7\sqrt{2}}{5\sqrt{61}}$

3. The sum of the roots of
    $(x - 800)(x - 16) = 0$

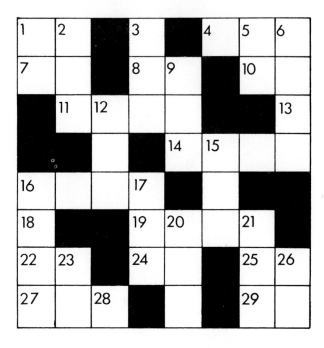

5. The smallest integer whose square best approximates 200

6. $n^3 (n + 3)(2n + 7)^2$ where n is a solution of $10x^2 - 40 = 0,\ x > 0$

9. The product of the roots of
    $x^2 - 29x + 208 = 4$

12. $a(10^2) + a(10^1) + a(10^0)$ where a is the smallest prime factor of 10,567,036

15. Five times a power of two.

16. [(10 ACROSS) $-$ 20] [(7 ACROSS) $-$ 3]

17. Twice the factors of 406

20. Each digit is a different power of two.

21. The product of the roots of
    $(x - 2^5)(x - 23) = 0$

23. x where $2x^2 - 54x - 56 = 0$

26. The product of the excluded values of
    $\dfrac{x^3 - 9x^2 - 9x - 11}{(x - 9)^2 (x - 11)}$

28. The lowest common prime factor of 126 and 1100

104

ALGEBRA ADAGE

A television Antenna, mounted on a flat roof, is supported by cables. If the cables come from 40 feet up on the pole to nine feet from the base, then A is the length of the cables.

The length of the diagonal of a Cardboard Carton 3″ high, 4″ wide, and 12″ long is C inches.

Three squares are different sizes. Each touches the other at only one vertex and one pair touch at right angles. The areas of the squares are 576, 625, and E (which is smallest).

$\overline{41}\ \overline{48}\ \overline{41}\ \overline{48}\ \overline{13}\ \overline{36}\ \overline{49}\ \overline{48}\ \overline{17}$ $\overline{13}\ \overline{41}\ \overline{48}\ \overline{36}\ \overline{48}\ \overline{49}$ $\overline{13}\ \overline{41}\ \overline{48}\ \overline{17}$

$\overline{}\ \overline{49}\ \overline{36}\ \overline{48}\ \overline{7}\ \overline{17}\ \overline{37}$ $\overline{13}\ \overline{17}\ \overline{49}\ \overline{}$ $\overline{36}\ \overline{48}\ \overline{65}\ \overline{37}\ \overline{49}\ \overline{7}\ \overline{5}$

$\overline{7}\ \overline{17}\ \overline{37}\ \overline{41}\ \overline{17}\ \overline{41}\ \overline{42}\ \overline{49}\ \overline{67}$.

F is how Far it is between (−19, 4) and (37, −29).

A vacant corner lot is 60 by 91 and a favorite shortcut diagonally across. G is the distance Gained by the shortcut.

The sides of a right triangle are consecutive integers. H is the longest side.

$$I^2 + (2I + 5)^2 = (3I - 23)^2.$$

On the baseball diamond, the bases are 90 feet apart and the pitcher's Mound is 60 feet from home plate. M is the distance (to the nearest foot) from the Mound to second base.

N is the Number of inches in the shortest side of a rectangle one yard one foot seven inches wide and a two yard one inch diagonal.

R is the length of the diagonal of a Rectangle 35 by 12.

In a right triangle the hypotenuse is just one unit longer than the longer side and that side is three more than three times the shorter side S.

A Television Tube is 8″ high and 15″ wide but the Tube is measured diagonally as T inches.

CROSSWORD PUZZLE

RADICALS

ACROSS

1. The decimal for $\frac{1}{128}$ ___?___
8. Piece of 3.1416
9. Jolly laugh
10. An idiot tube
11. Grade point average (abbr.)
12. Strength of a number
14.

$$\frac{\sqrt{R^2}\ \sqrt[4]{H^4}\ \sqrt[3]{E^6}}{\sqrt{E^2}}$$

15. __?__ , a drop of golden sun
16. Unity
17. "____" Boy
19. 17 ACROSS multiplied by D equals information.
20. $\sqrt[3]{3375}$ and 15 are __?__
23. $a + \sqrt{16}$ and $a - \sqrt{16}$
26. Uninteresting
27. Musical note
28. The denominator of 8 ACROSS when it is written in approximate fraction form.
29. 10

DOWN

1. Indian home
2. 2(24 DOWN - 25 DOWN)(a)
3. $\sqrt{\frac{1}{9}}$ is a ___?___ decimal
5. Inverse of "Yep"
6. t^2
7. Opposite of odd
13. The set of all rationals and irrationals form the set of ___?___ numbers.
14. $\sqrt{}$
15. __?__ , __?__ , __?__ your boat
18. 625 is a perfect ___?___ .
21. $\sqrt{169} - \sqrt{25} = $ __?__
22. $\sqrt[3]{(ice)^3} = $ the __?__ root of ice cube
24. $\sqrt{50} + \sqrt{338} - \sqrt{128} = $ __?__ $\sqrt{2}$
25. 29 ACROSS - $\sqrt[4]{256}$

ALGEBRA ADAGE

$$\overline{11}\ \overline{10}\ \overline{6}\quad \overline{-14}\ \overline{-6}\ \overline{-1}\quad \overline{-14}\ \overline{11}\ \overline{6}\ \overline{9}\ \overline{11}$$

$$\overline{13}\ \overline{6}\ \overline{5}\ \overline{11}\ \overline{10}\ \overline{6}\ \overline{-6}\ \overline{6}\ \overline{-12}\quad \overline{15}\ \overline{2}\ \overline{-14}\ \overline{6}\ \overline{-12}$$

$$\overline{9}\ \overline{6}\ \overline{2}\ \overline{}\quad \overline{6}\ \overline{9}\quad \overline{11}\ \overline{10}\ \overline{6}\quad \overline{5}\ \overline{14}\ \overline{14}\ \overline{6}\ \overline{4}\ \overline{2}\ \overline{-12}.$$

A = $(6-\sqrt6)(3\sqrt2-2\sqrt3)(4\sqrt2+3\sqrt3)/6$

B = $\sqrt3(\sqrt{27}+\sqrt{48}-\sqrt{12})$

D = $(\sqrt6+\sqrt3)(\sqrt6-2\sqrt3)(\sqrt8)$

E = $(\sqrt{8-2\sqrt7})(\sqrt{8+2\sqrt7})$

F = $(4+\sqrt3)(4-\sqrt3)$

H = $(\sqrt2-\sqrt3)^2+(\sqrt2+\sqrt3)^2$

I = $(2-\sqrt3)(\sqrt3+1)^2$

L = $(3-\sqrt5)(\sqrt5+3)$

N = $(2+\sqrt2)(3-\sqrt2)(4-\sqrt2)$

O = $(4)(½+½\sqrt2)(½-½\sqrt2)$

FIND THE VALUE OF THE CAPITAL LETTERS DEFINED AND REPLACE THE VALUES UNDER THE BLANKS BY THE CORRESPONDING LETTER. ONCE YOU HAVE DISCOVERED THE ALGEBRA ADAGE, ATTEMPT TO REPHRASE IT AS A COMMON PROVERB. NOTICE THAT A COUPLE OF BLANKS ARE WITHOUT NUMERICAL CLUES AND MUST BE FOUND BY INFERENCE.

P = $(2+\sqrt6)(3+\sqrt2)(2-\sqrt6)(3-\sqrt2)$

R = $(2\sqrt3-3\sqrt2)(3\sqrt2+2\sqrt3)$

S = $\dfrac{(2\sqrt3-\sqrt6)(3\sqrt3+3\sqrt6)}{\sqrt2}$

T = $\dfrac{2\sqrt3-1}{\sqrt3+2}(5\sqrt3+8)$

107

THESE **ALPHAMETICS** MAY BURN YOU!! HEH, HEH!!

$$ICE = \sqrt{IGLOO}$$

$$\sqrt{STARCH} = FAT$$

$$\sqrt{THREE} = TWO$$

$$(AN)^5 = EQUATION$$

```
  SEVEN
  SEVENS
  ------
  FORTY9
```

```
  EIGHT
  TIMES
  EIGHT
  -----
  SIXTY4
```

$$\frac{EVE}{DID} = .\overline{TALKTALKTALK}$$

MATCHSTICKS

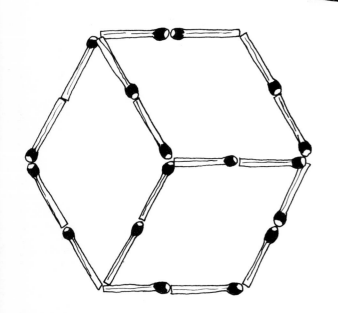

MOVE FOUR MATCHES AND FORM TWO CONGRUENT SHAPES INSTEAD OF THE THREE SHOWN.

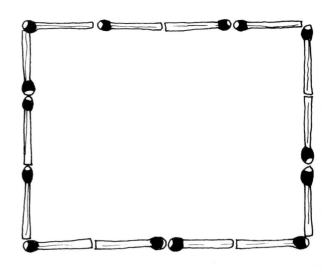

ADD FIVE MORE MATCHES SO THAT THE INTERIOR OF THE RECTANGLE IS DIVIDED INTO TWO SECTORS OF EQUAL AREA. DO THIS IN AT LEAST THREE DISTINCT WAYS.

$$\overline{}_{-9}\ \overline{}_{2}\ \overline{}_{3}\ \overline{}_{12}\ \overline{}_{-3}\ \overline{}_{-4}\ \overline{}_{4}\ \overline{}_{1}\ \overline{}_{5}\ \overline{}_{-8}\ \overline{}_{-2}\qquad \overline{}_{15}\ \overline{}_{1}\ \overline{}_{9}\ \overline{}_{6}\ \overline{}_{-11}$$

$$\overline{}_{14}\ \overline{}_{7}\ \overline{}_{10}\ \overline{}_{27}\qquad \overline{}_{8}\ \overline{}_{-4}\ \overline{}_{-2}\ \overline{}_{1}\ \overline{}_{15}\ \overline{}_{2}\ \overline{}_{3}\qquad \overline{}_{0}\ \overline{}_{-3}\ \overline{}_{9}\ \overline{}_{-6}\ \overline{}_{4}\ \overline{}_{2}$$

$$\overline{}_{10}\ \overline{}_{27}\ \overline{}_{1}\ \overline{}_{5}\qquad \overline{}_{-6}\ \overline{}_{15}\ \overline{}_{10}\ \overline{}_{-2}\ \overline{}_{-4}\ \overline{}_{1}\ \overline{}_{5}\ \overline{}_{-8}\ \overline{}_{2}\ \overline{}_{11}\ .$$

SOLVE THE FOLLOWING EQUATIONS FOR CLUES TO COMPLETING THE ALGEBRA ADAGE. BE CERTAIN TO CHECK FOR EXTRANEOUS SOLUTIONS.

$$\sqrt{A + 3} + \sqrt{A} = \frac{3}{\sqrt{A}}$$

$$\sqrt[3]{27C} + 6 = 0$$

$$\sqrt{E^2 + 5} - 3 = 0$$

$$\sqrt{F - 3} + 1 = 4$$

$$4 + \sqrt{\frac{G}{2}} = 6$$

$$\sqrt{\frac{H}{3}} - 2 = 1$$

$$\sqrt{\frac{3I - 1}{5}} = 2$$

$$2\sqrt{3(K - 3)} = K$$

$$L - 2 = \sqrt{6L - 5}$$

$$\sqrt{M - 3} = 5 - M$$

$$\sqrt{N - 1} = N - 3$$

$$\sqrt{2\varnothing + 7} = \varnothing + 4$$

$$7 + 2\sqrt[3]{3P} = 1$$

$$\sqrt{R^2 + R + 4} = 4$$

$$\sqrt[3]{S^2 + 4} = 5$$

$$5\sqrt{T - 6} = T$$

$$\sqrt{3 - U} - 9 = U$$

$$\sqrt{V + 2} = \sqrt{V} + \sqrt{2}$$

$$\sqrt{W + 2} - 2 = 2$$

$$\sqrt{X + 12} + \sqrt{X} = 2$$

NOW TRANSLATE THE ALGEBRA ADAGE INTO THE PROVERB IT PARAPHRASES.

HERE'S ANOTHER

ALGEBRA SEARCH

IT CONTAINS MORE THAN 50 WORDS DEALING WITH FACTOR- ING, FRACTIONS, RADICALS AND QUADRATICS.

```
R E D U C E B A S E M E R T X E
T N E N O P X E R E W O P C Q T
C C N C X R I L G R A P H U U A
T O O R O I S B W G L Y A B A N
Z N M E V M E A N E A T L E D I
L S I P F E M R A D I C A L R M
A T N E L F M O N O M I A L A I
C A A A A E I T N I O S S E T R
O N T T N V X C W T N S Q E I C
R T O I O I E A I O I E U R C S
P E R N I F D F M E B X A H N I
I R E G T L A I M O N I R T E D
C M Z E C O N J U G A T E N V V
E Z I L A N O I T A R R I I E E
R G C F R A D I C A N D Z N S N
Y T R O F O U R O T A R E M U N
```

HERE'S A LITTLE EXTRA. SIMPLIFY THE FOLLOWING IN AS SIMPLE A WAY AS POSSIBLE. NOTHING RADICAL! ! !

$$\sqrt{169 + 15\sqrt{77}} - \sqrt{(5\sqrt{11} - 13\sqrt{2})(3\sqrt{7} - 13\sqrt{2})}$$

SCRAMBLES

TRY MAKING SOME RADICAL CHANGES TO THESE!

1. NOT A LIAR

2. A QUIET NO

3. NUN, KNOW!

4. SCALD AIR

5. SYRINGE* + DECEM + CONSUME

— — — — — — — — — — — —

6. ALLOWANCE + ARTICLE + GIRL'S NAME + EAST*

— — — — — — — — — — — —

7. SWINDLE + CONTAINER + CORRODED

— — — — — — — — — — — —

TRY SIMPLIFYING THESE

WORD REBUSES

TO MATH TERMS THAT PERTAIN TO RADICALS.

8. IRELAND* + RODENT + CHARGED PARTICLE + CAPONE

— — — — — — — — —

9. ADDITIONAL + 100 + Sn + GRAM*

— — — — — — — — —

10. REGARDING* + A VEGETABLE + AN ECHOIC

— — — — — —

Quadratics

Chapter Preview - Quadratics

Page	Activity

ALGEBRA ADAGE

1. $(A + 6)^2 = 4A^2$

2. $7C + 15 = 4C^2$

3.   D is the discriminant of:
$$3x^2 - 7x + 4 = 0$$

4. $x^2 + 1 = 4x$
$$x = E \pm F$$

5. $x^2 + 8x = 65$
$$x = H + I$$

6. $\dfrac{L^2 - 16}{L + 4} = 0$

7. $3R^2 = 5 - 14R$

8.   S is the sum of the roots of:
$$2x^2 + 6x = 4$$

9. $64x^2 + 16x = 35$
$$x = \dfrac{T}{Y}$$

10. $x^2 + \sqrt{7}x = 14$
$$x^2 = U$$

SOLVE THE EQUATIONS ABOVE TO FIND CLUES TO THE ALGEBRA ADAGE BELOW. NOTICE THAT SOME VARIABLES MAY HAVE MORE THAN ONE VALUE AND THAT SEVERAL BLANKS ARE WITHOUT NUMERICAL CLUES AND MUST BE FOUND BY INFERENCE. WHEN FINISHED, TRANSLATE THE ALGEBRA ADAGE INTO THE PROVERB IT PARAPHRASES.

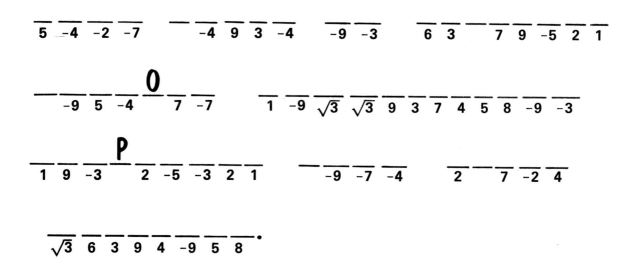

CROSSNUMBER PUZZLE

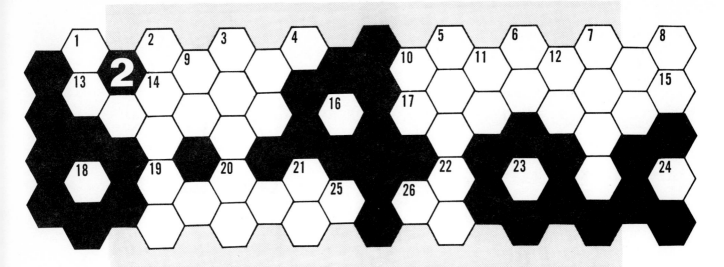

4. Square root of a perfect cube
16. A root of: $x - \sqrt{x = 6}$
18. $\sqrt[3]{343}$
23. A root of: $\sqrt{2x} + x - 12 = 0$
24. The radicand when the following is simplified:

$$-6\sqrt{\frac{10}{18}} + 8\sqrt{\frac{15}{48}} - 10\sqrt{\frac{35}{28}}$$

↓ 1 2 3

1. $|x|$ where $2x^2 - 14x - 156 = 0$
6. If the roots of a quadratic are $(-4, -9)$, then what is the constant term if the coefficient of x^2 is one?
7. The value of the discriminant of: $2x^2 + 34x - 9 = 0$
9. $x^2 - .14x = -.0049$, $x = .\underline{\ ?\ }$
11. $(6 \downarrow) - (1 \downarrow)$
12. The sum of the roots of: $3x^2 + 1152 = 63x$

↓ 1 2 3

2. The 46th triangular number
3. The radicand in the solution of:
$$\frac{2}{x} + \frac{x}{x + 4} = 2$$
7. The product of the roots of: $3x^2 - 27x + 222 = -234$
10. $(12 \downarrow)(1 \downarrow)$
13. A palindromic cube
14. $5177717^{1/3}$
17. $9x^2 + 6 = 9$, $x = .\underline{\ ?\ }$
19. A perfect square whose digits add to be a multiple of 5
26. Mr. Wrong had one hour to drive to an appointment 50 miles from home. He traveled 30 miles and then realized he would have to increase his speed by 15 mph for the remainder of his trip. What was his speed for the first 30 miles?

↙ 1 2 3

5. A root of: $x^2 - 484 = 0$
8. What you add to solve the following quadratic by completing the square: $x^2 + 78x = 32$
15. The product of the roots of:
$x^2 - 7x + 11 = 0$
and
$x^2 - 13x + 22 = 0$
20. The value of the discriminant for: $3x^2 = -22 - 25x$
21. $|(15 \nearrow) - (13 \searrow)|$
22. A multiple of 8 and the positive number found by the following:
Three times the reciprocal of a number is one-twelfth the sum of the number and nine.
25. $[(10 \searrow) - (14 \searrow)]^{1/2}$

____ ____   ____ ____ ____ ____ ____   ____ ____ ____   ____ ____   ____ ____

4.2   1.3   .14   .13   .12   .58   .09   –.8   .84   1.9   2.1   .14   –1.1

____ ____ ____ ____ ____ ____ ____ ____ ____ ____   ____ ____   ____ ____ ____ ____

.31   –.8   1.6   1.3   .58   –.7   1.2   –.6   2.1   1.4   –.8   –.5   .31   .14   1.2   1.5

SOLVE EACH OF THE FOLLOWING QUADRATIC EQUATIONS AND APPROXIMATE THE ROOTS WITH TABLES OR CALCULATOR. REPLACE EACH DECIMAL WITH THE CORRESPONDING CAPITAL LETTER AND DISCOVER THE ALGEBRA ADAGE.

$9A^2 + 6A = 1$

$4B^2 = 8B - 1$

$12C = 9C^2 + 1$

$25D^2 = 48$

$9E^2 - 24E + 11 = 0$

$5F^2 + 2 = 8F$

$15H^2 - H - 6 = 0$

$L^2 = 8L + 1$

$2N^2 + 10N + 7 = 0$

$5R^2 = 8R$

$25S^2 + 40S + 13 = 0$

$20T + 28 = 25T^2$

NOW TRANSLATE THE ALGEBRA ADAGE INTO A COMMON PROVERB.

CROSSWORD PUZZLE

ACROSS

1. $x^2 - 24x + 143 = 0$, x = ?
10. Sum of one or more terms
12. Sum of the roots of:
    $16x^2 - 320x + 1599 = 0$
13. Product of the roots of:
    $x^2 - 6x + 6 = 0$
14. abbr. (see 17 DOWN)
15. Root of 3 DOWN with 41 DOWN
16. Clamor
17. (41 DOWN) (follows Q) (24 ACROSS)
18. Who, what, ___?___ when, why (put on!)
20. Plural of 27 ACROSS if second degree
24. Union
25. Twelve seats back
27. 10 ACROSS with exactly three across
30. Absolute value of the product of the
    roots of $x^2 + \sqrt{2}x - 2 = 0$
31. Japanese game
32. N4
33. CX
34. $2x^2 + 2\sqrt{6}x + 3$ is the ___?___
    of $\sqrt{2}x + \sqrt{3}$.
36. Prefix for eight
37. No backwards
38. Bunch of sticks
40. 20 ACROSS ___?___ have no real roots

DOWN

1. Permutation of pet
2. Decrease the value of u
3. $x^2 - 2ex + e^2 = x^2 - 2Lx + L^2$
   then ___ and ___ are ___ ___
4. Phonetic win (with a German accent)
5. Permutation of 10
6. Permutation of LOAN YE
7. The value 12 in 13 ACROSS
8. A set of gloves
9. 1st degree term in $y^2 + 160y - 15$
11. $x^2 - (m + n)x + mn = 0$, x = ?
17. Statement of equality
18. Rights and ___?___
19. Smallest component of an element
21. Permutation of rid
22. People holder
23. Work out
28. x is a factor ___?___ in x^2
29. $o^2 q$
35. Permutation of flying saucer
39. $s^2 - 2st + t^2 = 0$, s = ?
40. Exclamation
41. Root of 3 DOWN
42. See 11 DOWN

118

ALGEBRA ADAGE

$$\overline{}\ \overline{}\ \overline{}\ \overline{}\qquad\overline{}\ \overline{}\ \overline{}\qquad\overline{}\ \overline{}\ \overline{}\ \overline{}\ \overline{}\ \overline{}$$
-5 3 1 6   -9 -5 6   -2 6 1 3 9 6

3 -8   -3 2 -8 6 9 -9   -9 -5 6

8 -1 5 6 9 -9 -8   7 -3 11 2 -1 1 .

**FIND THE VALUES OF THE CAPITAL LETTERS IN THE PROBLEMS BELOW
AND REPLACE THE BLANKS ABOVE TO DISCOVER THE ALGEBRA ADAGE.**

$9a^2 + 18a - 17 = 0$

$a = \dfrac{A \pm \sqrt{26}}{-A}$

$4b^2 = 12b - 7$

$b = \dfrac{-A \pm \sqrt{B}}{B}$

$5d^2 - 4d - 2 = 0$

$d = \dfrac{B \pm \sqrt{14}}{D}$

$6e^2 - 12e + 5 = 0$

$e = \dfrac{E \pm \sqrt{E}}{E}$

$f^2 + 4f = 3$

$f = F \pm \sqrt{G}$

A = _____
B = _____
D = _____
E = _____
F = _____
G = _____
H = _____
I = _____
L = _____
M = _____
N = _____
Ø = _____
R = _____
S = _____
T = _____

$h^2 + 10h + 22 = 0$

$h = H \pm \sqrt{I}$

$m^2 - 2m - 10 = 0$

$m = L \pm \sqrt{M}$

$x = \dfrac{B \pm \sqrt{D}}{A}$

$Nx^2 + 12x + \emptyset = 0$

$y = \dfrac{4 \pm \sqrt{88}}{8}$

$Ry^2 + Sy + T = 0$

PALATABLE PLOTTING

		ALTERNATE FORM	
$y - 2 = -(x - 2)^2$	$: y \geqslant -2$	$y = -x^2 + 4x - 2$	$: y \geqslant -2$
$y - 14 = -(x - 4)^2$	$: 0 \leqslant x \leqslant 8$	$y = -x^2 + 8x - 2$	$: |x - 4| \leqslant 4$
$y - 2 = -(x - 10)^2$	$: 8 \leqslant x \leqslant 12$	$y = -x^2 + 20x - 98$	$: |x - 10| \leqslant 2$
$y - 2 = -(x + 2)^2$	$: y \geqslant -2$	$y = -x^2 - 4x - 2$	$: |x + 2| \leqslant 2$
$y + 14 = (1/2)(x - 6)^2$	$: y \leqslant -12$	$2y = x^2 - 12x + 8$	$: |x - 6| < 2$
$y - 2 = -(x - 6)^2$	$: 4 \leqslant x \leqslant 8$	$y = -x^2 + 12x - 34$	$: |y| \leqslant 2$
$x = 4$	$: -12 \leqslant y \leqslant 14$	$x - 4 = 0$	$: |y - 1| \leqslant 13$
$y - 14 = (-1/4)(x - 4)^2$	$: y \geqslant -2$	$4y = -x^2 + 8x + 40$	$: |x - 4| \leqslant 8$

GRAPH EACH OF THE EQUATIONS ABOVE ON THE COORDINATE AXES PROVIDED.

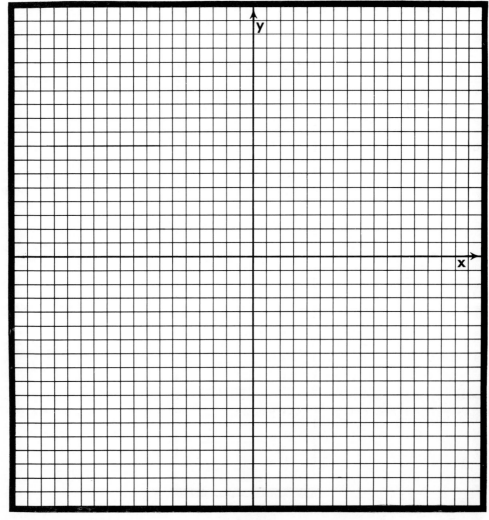

120

PALATABLE PLOTTING

$(x + 4)^2 + (y - 1)^2 = 4$

$(x - 12)^2 + (y - 7)^2 = 36$: $y \leqslant 7$

$(x + 4)^2 + (y + 4)^2 = 16$: $y \leqslant -4$

$(x - 4)^2 + (y - 7)^2 = 64$: $y \geqslant 7$

$(x + 4)^2 + (y + 3)^2 = 49$: $y \leqslant 5$

$(x + 4)^2 + (y + 3)^2 = 100$: $y \geqslant 5$

$(x - 15)^2 + (y - 7)^2 = 9$: $y \leqslant 7$

$(x + 4)^2 + (y + 10)^2 = 52$: $y \geqslant -4$

$(x - 1)^2 + (y - 7)^2 = 25$: $y \geqslant 7$

$y = -8$: $-7 \leqslant x \leqslant -5$ or $-3 \leqslant x \leqslant -1$

$x = -4$: $-10 \leqslant y \leqslant -8$

$(x + 8)(x + 1) = 0$: $-14 \leqslant y \leqslant -12$

$y + 15 = (-1/6)(x - 5)$: $-1 \leqslant x \leqslant 5$

$y + 14 = (1/6)(x + 7)$: $-15 \leqslant y \leqslant -14$

$(x + 4)^2 + (y - 1)^2 = 4$

$(x - 12)^2 + (y - 7)^2 = 36$: $y \leqslant 7$

$(x + 4)^2 + (y + 4)^2 = 16$: $y \leqslant -4$

$(x - 4)^2 + (y - 7)^2 = 64$: $y \geqslant 7$

$(x + 4)^2 + (y + 3)^2 = 49$: $y \leqslant 5$

$x^2 + y^2 + 8x + 6y - 75 = 0$: $y \geqslant 5$

$x^2 + y^2 - 30x - 14y + 265 = 0$: $y \leqslant 7$

$x^2 + y^2 + 8x + 20y + 64 = 0$: $y \geqslant -4$

$x^2 + y^2 - 2x - 14y + 25 = 0$: $y \geqslant 7$

$y + 8 = 0$: $|x + 6| \leqslant 1$ or $|x + 2| \leqslant 1$

$x + 4 = 0$: $|y + 9| \leqslant 1$

$x^2 + 9x + 8 = 0$: $|y + 13| \leqslant 1$

$(x - 5) + 6(y + 15) = 0$: $|x - 2| \leqslant 3$

$(x + 13) - 6(y + 15) = 0$: $|2y + 29| \leqslant 1$

GRAPH EACH OF THE EQUATIONS ABOVE ON THE COORDINATE AXES PROVIDED.

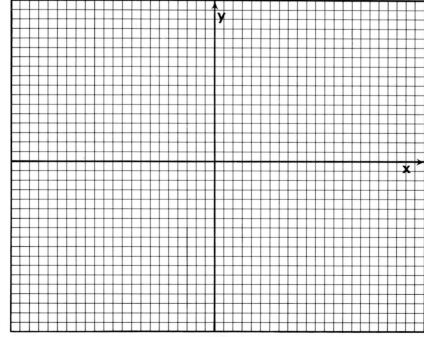

ALPHAMETICS

```
  TRACK
  SPACE
 ───────
  ROCKET
```

```
  MOON
  MEN
  CAN
 ───────
  REACH
```

```
  NOW
  TWO
  IN
  TWIN
 ───────
  ORBIT
```

```
  SEE
  SPACE
  CRAFT
  PASSES
 ────────
  NEPTUNE
```

```
  URANUS
  SATURN
 ────────
  JUPITER
```

```
  FLAME
  OUT
 ───────
  WOES
```

```
  NURSE
  SEES
  SUN
 ───────
  SHOTS
```

```
  TRUST
  UFO
  NOT
  TRUE
 ───────
  SAUCER
```

SCRAMBLES

SULFUR + 5280 FEET

OR
GREEK [abbr.] + INCH

1. A CARD QUIT

2. TIM C. RAIDS INN

3.† CREOLE MAP QUEST

4.† TROD SAND FARM

5.† RUM FOR AQUATIC LAD

6.† QUEER CARP FEST

WORD REBUSES

7. PREFIX FOR FOUR + SUN GOD + _?_ TOC

— — — — — — — — —

8. LP RECORD + EDGE + INDIUM* + INSECT

— — — — — — — — — — — —

9. SHAPE + A VOWEL + LOS ANGELES*

— — — — — — — —

10. PENNSYLVANIA* + RADIUM* + BODY ODOR* + LOUISIANA*

— — — — — — — —

†Two words
*Abbreviation

GLOSSARY OF SPECIAL TYPES OF NUMBERS

Factorial numbers

A factorial number is a natural number which is the product of consecutive natural numbers beginning with one and ending with the specified number.

$0! = 1$, by definition.
$1! = 1$
$2! = 2 = 1 \cdot 2$
$3! = 6 = 1 \cdot 2 \cdot 3$
$4! = 24 = 1 \cdot 2 \cdot 3 \cdot 4$

Fibonacci numbers

The Fibonacci numbers are an infinite sequence of natural numbers in which each is the sum of the preceding two, where the first two are both one.

$1, 1, 2, 3, 5, 8, 13, 21, 34, 55, 89, \ldots$

If the first two terms are taken as one and three, the **Lucas numbers** are generated.

$1, 3, 4, 7, 11, 18, 29, 47, 76, \ldots$

Figurate numbers

The figurate numbers are natural number sequences which count the number of points in regular polygonal arrangements and thus are also called **Polygonal numbers.**

Triangular numbers

$$1, \quad 3, \quad 6, \quad 10, \ldots, \frac{n(n+1)}{2}$$

Square numbers

$$1, \quad 4, \quad 9, \quad 16, \ldots, n^2$$

Pentagonal numbers

$$1, \quad 5, \quad 12, \quad 22, \ldots, \frac{n(3n-1)}{2}$$

Hexagonal numbers

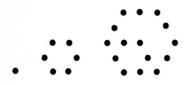

$$1, \quad 6, \quad 15, \quad 28, \ldots, n(2n-1)$$

Palindromic numbers

A palindrome is a natural number of two or more digits which is the same if the order of the digits is reversed.

11, 232, 4554, 67876, . . .

(MADAM I'M ADAM is a word palindrome.)

Perfect numbers

A perfect number is any natural number which is equal to the sum of its proper divisors. (That is, all the whole number divisors except the number itself.)

$$6 = 1 + 2 + 3$$
$$28 = 1 + 2 + 4 + 7 + 14$$
$$496$$
$$8128$$

Euler's Formula for perfect numbers: $P_n = 2^{n-1}(2^n - 1)$ provided $(2^n - 1)$ is prime.

Amicable numbers

Two natural numbers are said to be amicable (or friendly) if each is equal to the sum of the proper divisors of the other.

220 and 284 are amicable.

Pythagorean numbers

Pythagorean numbers are triplets of natural numbers which are sides of a right triangle.

(3,4,5), (5,12,13), (8,15,17), and (7,24,25) are all pythagorean and can be verified by the Pythagorean Theorem.

Table of Primes

2	199	467	769	1087	1429	1741	2089	2437	2791	3187	3541	3911	4271
3	211	479	773	1091	1433	1747	2099	2441	2797	3191	3547	3917	4273
5	223	487	787	1093	1439	1753	2111	2447	2801	3203	3557	3919	4283
7	227	491	797	1097	1447	1759	2113	2459	2803	3209	3559	3923	4289
11	229	499	809	1103	1451	1777	2129	2467	2819	3217	3571	3929	4297
13	233	503	811	1109	1453	1783	2131	2473	2833	3221	3581	3931	4327
17	239	509	821	1117	1459	1787	2137	2477	2837	3229	3583	3943	4337
19	241	521	823	1123	1471	1789	2141	2503	2843	3251	3593	3947	4339
23	251	523	827	1129	1481	1801	2143	2521	2851	3253	3607	3967	4349
29	257	541	829	1151	1483	1811	2153	2531	2857	3257	3613	3989	4357
31	263	547	839	1153	1487	1823	2161	2539	2861	3259	3617	4001	4363
37	269	557	853	1163	1489	1831	2179	2543	2879	3271	3623	4003	4373
41	271	563	857	1171	1493	1847	2203	2549	2887	3299	3631	4007	4391
43	277	569	859	1181	1499	1861	2207	2551	2897	3301	3637	4013	4397
47	281	571	863	1187	1511	1867	2213	2557	2903	3307	3643	4019	4409
53	283	577	877	1193	1523	1871	2221	2579	2909	3313	3659	4021	4421
59	293	587	881	1201	1531	1873	2237	2591	2917	3319	3671	4027	4423
61	307	593	883	1213	1543	1877	2239	2593	2927	3323	3673	4049	4441
67	311	599	887	1217	1549	1879	2243	2609	2939	3329	3677	4051	4447
71	313	601	907	1223	1553	1889	2251	2617	2953	3331	3691	4057	4451
73	317	607	911	1229	1559	1901	2267	2621	2957	3343	3697	4073	4457
79	331	613	919	1231	1567	1907	2269	2633	2963	3347	3701	4079	4463
83	337	617	929	1237	1571	1913	2273	2647	2969	3359	3709	4091	4481
89	347	619	937	1249	1579	1931	2281	2657	2971	3361	3719	4093	4483
97	349	631	941	1259	1583	1933	2287	2659	2999	3371	3727	4099	4493
101	353	641	947	1277	1597	1949	2293	2663	3001	3373	3733	4111	4507
103	359	643	953	1279	1601	1951	2297	2671	3011	3389	3739	4127	4513
107	367	647	967	1283	1607	1973	2309	2677	3019	3391	3761	4129	4517
109	373	653	971	1289	1609	1979	2311	2683	3023	3407	3767	4133	4519
113	379	659	977	1291	1613	1987	2333	2687	3037	3413	3769	4139	4523
127	383	661	983	1297	1619	1993	2339	2689	3041	3433	3779	4153	4547
131	389	673	991	1301	1621	1997	2341	2693	3049	3449	3793	4157	4549
137	397	677	997	1303	1627	1999	2347	2699	3061	3457	3797	4159	4561
139	401	683	1009	1307	1637	2003	2351	2707	3067	3461	3803	4177	4567
149	409	691	1013	1319	1657	2011	2357	2711	3079	3463	3821	4201	4583
151	419	701	1019	1321	1663	2017	2371	2713	3083	3467	3823	4211	4591
157	421	709	1021	1327	1667	2027	2377	2719	3089	3469	3833	4217	4597
163	431	719	1031	1361	1669	2029	2381	2729	3109	3491	3847	4219	4603
167	433	727	1033	1367	1693	2039	2383	2731	3119	3499	3851	4229	4621
173	439	733	1039	1373	1697	2053	2389	2741	3121	3511	3853	4231	4637
179	443	739	1049	1381	1699	2063	2393	2749	3137	3517	3863	4241	4639
181	449	743	1051	1399	1709	2069	2399	2753	3163	3527	3877	4243	4643
191	457	751	1061	1409	1721	2081	2411	2767	3167	3529	3881	4253	4649
193	461	757	1063	1423	1723	2083	2417	2777	3169	3533	3889	4259	4651
197	463	761	1069	1427	1733	2087	2423	2789	3181	3539	3907	4261	4657

4663	5051	5449	5839	6229	6637	7001	7477	7841	8263	8681	9067	9463	9859
4673	5059	5471	5843	6247	6653	7013	7481	7853	8269	8689	9091	9467	9871
4679	5077	5477	5849	6257	6659	7019	7487	7867	8273	8693	9103	9473	9883
4691	5081	5479	5851	6263	6661	7027	7489	7873	8287	8699	9109	9479	9887
4703	5087	5483	5857	6269	6673	7039	7499	7877	8291	8707	9127	9491	9901
4721	5099	5501	5861	6271	6679	7043	7507	7879	8293	8713	9133	9497	9907
4723	5101	5503	5867	6277	6689	7057	7517	7883	8297	8719	9137	9511	9923
4729	5107	5507	5869	6287	6691	7069	7523	7901	8311	8731	9151	9521	9929
4733	5113	5519	5879	6299	6701	7079	7529	7907	8317	8737	9157	9533	9931
4751	5119	5521	5881	6301	6703	7103	7537	7919	8329	8741	9161	9539	9941
4759	5147	5527	5897	6311	6709	7109	7541	7927	8353	8747	9173	9547	9949
4783	5153	5531	5903	6317	6719	7121	7547	7933	8363	8753	9181	9551	9967
4787	5167	5557	5923	6323	6733	7127	7549	7937	8369	8761	9187	9587	9973
4789	5171	5563	5927	6329	6737	7129	7559	7949	8377	8779	9199	9601	
4793	5179	5569	5939	6337	6761	7151	7561	7951	8387	8783	9203	9613	
4799	5189	5573	5953	6343	6763	7159	7573	7963	8389	8803	9209	9619	
4801	5197	5581	5981	6353	6779	7177	7577	7993	8419	8807	9221	9623	
4813	5209	5591	5987	6359	6781	7187	7583	8009	8423	8819	9227	9629	
4817	5227	5623	6007	6361	6791	7193	7589	8011	8429	8821	9239	9631	
4831	5231	5639	6011	6367	6793	7207	7591	8017	8431	8831	9241	9643	
4861	5233	5641	6029	6373	6803	7211	7603	8039	8443	8837	9257	9649	
4871	5237	5647	6037	6379	6823	7213	7607	8053	8447	8839	9277	9661	
4877	5261	5651	6043	6389	6827	7219	7621	8059	8461	8849	9281	9677	
4889	5273	5653	6047	6397	6829	7229	7639	8069	8467	8861	9283	9679	
4903	5279	5657	6053	6421	6833	7237	7643	8081	8501	8863	9293	9689	
4909	5281	5659	6067	6427	7841	7243	7649	8087	8513	8867	9311	9697	
4919	5297	5669	6073	6449	6857	7247	7669	8089	8521	8887	9319	9719	
4931	5303	5683	6079	6451	6863	7253	7673	8093	8527	8893	9323	9721	
4933	5309	5689	6089	6469	6869	7283	7681	8101	8537	8923	9337	9733	
4937	5323	5693	6091	6473	6871	7297	7687	8111	8539	8929	9341	9739	
4943	5333	5701	6101	6481	6883	7307	7691	8117	8543	8933	9343	9743	
4951	5347	5711	6113	6491	6899	7309	7699	8123	8563	8941	9349	9749	
4957	5351	5717	6121	6521	6907	7321	7703	8147	8573	8951	9371	9767	
4967	5381	5737	6131	6529	6911	7331	7717	8161	8581	8963	9377	9769	
4969	5387	5741	6133	6547	6917	7333	7723	8167	8597	8969	9391	9781	
4973	5393	5743	6143	6551	6947	7349	7727	8171	8599	8971	9397	9787	
4987	5399	5749	6151	6553	6949	7351	7741	8179	8609	8999	9403	9791	
4993	5407	5779	6163	6563	6959	7369	7753	8191	8623	9001	9413	9803	
4999	5413	5783	6173	6569	6961	7393	7757	8209	8627	9007	9419	9811	
5003	5417	5791	6197	6571	6967	7411	7759	8219	8629	9011	9421	9817	
5009	5419	5801	6199	6577	6971	7417	7789	8221	8641	9013	9431	9829	
5011	5431	5807	6203	6581	6977	7433	7793	8231	8647	9029	9433	9833	
5021	5437	5813	6211	6599	6983	7451	7817	8233	8663	9041	9437	9839	
5023	5441	5821	6217	6607	6991	7457	7823	8237	8669	9043	9439	9851	
5039	5443	5827	6221	6619	6997	7459	7829	8243	8677	9059	9461	9857	

SOLUTIONS

Page 13, ALGEBRA ADAGE I

A PAIR IS A CONGENIAL
GROUP, BUT ONE MORE MAKES
A MOB.

Two's company, three's a crowd.

Page 14, CROSSWORD PUZZLE I

```
F O   E L E M E N T S
I D E A   B U   S H U
N D L   N U L L   R B
I N F I N I T E   E S
T U   S E M I F R E E
E M F   E M P T Y   T
  B I G   P L A N E S
S E V E N   E L E V
I R E D   C   O V E R
X S   C O U N T I N G
```

Page 15, ALGEBRA ADAGE II

ONE RED FRUIT OF THE MALUS
FAMILY INGESTED DAILY
HOLDS A MEDICAL DISCIPLE
AFAR.

An apple a day keeps the doctor
away.

Page 16, CROSSNUMBER PUZZLE I

Solution 1	Solution 2
2 3 5 7	3 3 5 7
1 9 6 3 8	1 9 6 3 8
1 4 1	1 9 1
9 4 8	9 4 8
4 3 2 4 9	6 3 2 4 9
6 2 2 1	6 2 2 1

Page 17, ALGEBRA ADAGE III

REFRAIN FROM ENUMERAT-
ING YOUR POULTRY PRIOR TO
THEIR EMERGENCE FROM
THEIR CALCIFIED ENCLO-
SURES.

Don't count your chickens before
they hatch.

Page 18, ALPHAMETICS

HE	10	ALAS	5157
SENT	2035	LASS	1577
HE	10	NO	38
SENT	2035	+ MORE	2804
THE	510	CASH	9576*
+ TEN	503		
THEN	5103		

*not unique

Page 19, ALPHAMETICS I

ZERO	9635	or	9635	TWO	106
ONE	546		586	THREE	19722
TWO	185		145	SEVEN	82524
THREE	10366		10366	TWELVE	102352

$$\text{TWO} \overline{)\text{TWELVE}} = \text{SIX} \qquad 367\overline{)360410} = 982$$

ONE	621	FORTY	29786
TWO	847	TEN	850
FIVE	9071	TEN	850
EIGHT	10538	SIXTY	31486

Page 20, ALGEBRA SEARCH I

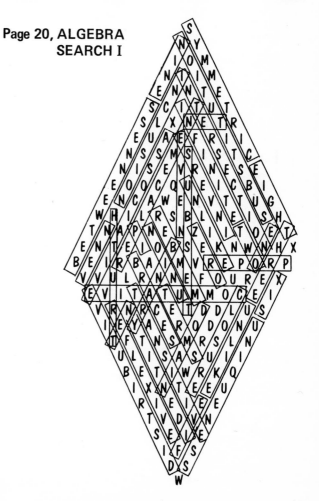

Page 21, SCRAMBLES I

1. Fundamentals
2. Associative
3. Subtraction
4. Distributive
5. Reflexive
6. Equivalent
8. I DENT IT Y
9. T RAN SIT IV E
10. DIST RIB U T IVE

Page 25, ALGEBRA ADAGE IV

AN ITEM OF LOVELINESS GIVES PERPETUAL PLEA-SURE.

A thing of beauty is a joy forever.

Page 26, CROSSWORD PUZZLE II

```
C L O S U R E    N E E D
S O    P L U S    F E W   I
W   U P   U   S I GN     R
A B S O L U T E V A L U E
M R   S I      V E T O   C
P O S I T I VE    I N I T
    W A T E R    N O V I C E
I N V E R S E    C E D E D
```

Page 27, ALGEBRA ADAGE V

A ROTATING FRAGMENT OF MINERALS COLLECTS NO BRYOPHYTIC PLANTS.

A rolling stone gathers no moss.

Page 28, CROSSNOMIAL PUZZLE I

```
2 y  - 5 x  - 1 2
x + 5 y + z + 5
-  x z  - 3 y z x
6 y  - 9 z + x
y + 4 x + 6 y z
-  8 x + 7 y     -
3 z + 2 y z     8
6 x y z     x z y
```

Page 29, MATCHSTICKS I

I   = III   – II

XI   = II

II – 0 = II

XI   = II

Page 29, ALPHAMETICS II

TRIAL	71438
AND	329
ERROR	61101
AT	37
RANDOM	132905

TEST	5025	MORE	1976
ALL	988	MORE	1976
THE	560	MORE	1976
ALPHA	98769	IN	43
METICS	105342	FORM	5971

Page 30, CROSSNUMBER PUZZLE II

```
2 2 3   3   4 7 7
3 3   9 8 1   2 2
7 3 3   3   3 5 4
9   8 3   4 1   3
  4 4 7 1 9 2 1
2 2 4 1   6 2 5 6
3 3 4   5   7 3 3
1 5   8 4 8   1 1
1 6 2   4   9 4 2
```

Page 31, SCRAMBLES II

1. Positive
2. Negative
3. Magnitude
4. Absolute Value
5. IN VERSE
6. NE GAT IVE
7. PO SIT IV E
8. SIGN ED NUMB ER

Page 35, ALGEBRA ADAGE VI

RETIRING AND RISING WITH PROMPTITUDE CREATES ONE WHO IS SALUTARY OPULENT AND ERUDITE.

Early to bed, early to rise, makes one healthy, wealthy, and wise.

Page 36, CROSSNOMIAL PUZZLE II

1	6	x^2	3	5	2
	x^2	+	3	x	+	2
x^2	-	2	x	-	3	5
	5	x	+	4	x^2	-	9
5	x	-	3	4	+	6	x^2
1	-	x^3	x^2	1	4
2	6	-	x	-	6	x^2
x^3	3	+	3	x

Page 37, ALGEBRA ADAGE VII

REPEATED EXERCISE CREATES EXCELLENCE.

Practice makes perfect.

Page 38, MATCHSTICKS II

1. $2 - 9 + 8 = 1$
2. $7 - 3 - 3 = 1$
3. $3 - 5 + 3 = 1$
4. $72 = 85 - 13$
5.
6.
7.
8. 20

Page 39-40, CROSSWORD PUZZLE III

```
  FOUR   MINI
 NINETY  NINE
SEVEN OX EVEN
EVE  ENITCE I
NEG DQ  RESIN
SR FOURMA T E
EQUIVALENT I
 AVETALSO NT
RTRE I TPUAVH
AH TWO  ORDER
PRETENSES ORE
SEVEN TAENRSE
 EERIE R ONE
  NM DONUTS
```

Page 41, CROSSNUMBER PUZZLE III

```
4 4   1 4 0   5 1
3 9 2  9  3 4 3
 1 3 1  7 2 0
6  3 9 4  3 4 1
2 3  2 9 9  5 2
8 1 1  6 6 7  0
 4 4 1  9 9 7
3 1 3  2  8 9 9
3 6  1 8 6  7 7
```

Page 42, ALPHAMETICS III

ANTS	4129
CANT	5412
SCAN	9541

FIRS	9063
FOR	976
THE	584
BIRDS	10623

SEE	933
THE	263
	2799
	5598
	1866
	245379

Page 42, ALGEBRA SEARCH II

zero	twenty-three
one	twenty-seven
two	seventy-two
three	seventy-three
five	seventy-seven
seven	ninety
nine	ninety-two
ten	ninety-three
eleven	ninety-seven
twelve	
seventeen	one-seventh
nineteen	one-ninth
twenty	one-tenth
twenty-two	and so on

Page 43, SCRAMBLES III

1. Variable
2. Constant
3. Trinomial
4. Polynomial
5. FACT OR
6. POW ER(G)
7. EXPRESS I ON
8. BI NO MI AL

Page 47, ALGEBRA ADAGE VIII

THE PROMPTEST FEATHERED BIPED SEIZES THE ANNELID.

The early bird gets the worm.

Page 48, CROSSWORD PUZZLE IV

```
D I R E C T I O N
R N T   W O N D E R
F I V E   T W E L V E
O N E   E   E Q U A L
U K R   Q   R U   D A
R   S W U N G A B A T
  R E C I P   L M   I
. S O S   V   O I L   O
  I T   F A I N T S U N
X     I L L E Y E S
    S E V E N     S E T
    T W E N T Y F I V E
G R E A T E R T H A N
```

Page 49, ALGEBRA ADAGE IX

DISTANT MEADOWS ARE INEVITABLY MORE VERDANT.

The grass is always greener on the other side of the fence.

Page 50, MATCHSTICKS III

NINE
IV + I = V
III + I = IV
VI + IV = X
VI = X - IV
39 - 31 = 8
45 + 24 = 69
23 x 17 = 391

Page 51, ALGEBRA ADAGE X

EVERYTHING IS LEGITIMATE IN MATTERS PERTAINING TO ARDENT AFFECTION AND ARMED CONFLICT BETWEEN NATIONS.

All is fair in love and war.

Page 52, ALPHAMETICS IV

```
NO      82        EVEN    9892
IF      74         ODD     527
       328       PRIME   10469
       574
      6068
```

```
THIS    4765    or    4865
SURE    5809          5709
  IS      65            65
PRIME  10639         10639
```

```
RED     321          IT       23
FOR     563        TOOK     3881
      180723        THE      349
                   HINT     4253
```

AS / WISE / AS   32 / 1024 / 32

Page 53, SCRAMBLES IV

1. Roots
2. Equivalent
3. Unconditional
4. Solution Set
5. Conditional
6. LES ST HA N
7. TRANS POSE
8. RE CI PRO CAL
9. IN EQUAL IT Y
10. EQUI VA LENT

Page 57, ALGEBRA ADAGE XI

A FERROUS ALLOY ROPE OF INTERLOCKING LOOPS IS ONLY AS HEARTY AS ITS LEAST POTENT SECTION.

A chain is only as strong as its weakest link.

Page 58, CROSSNOMIAL PUZZLE III

3	x	–	3	y	=	8		
2	x	+	4	y	+	9	=	0
x	–	3	y	=	2	0	1	
–	5	y	=	6	x	+	3	0
7	y	+	2	x	=	2	8	
y	=	3	4	–	1	7	x	
=	1	6	–	8	0	x	+	y
7	5		x				y	

Page 59, ALGEBRA ADAGE XII

AN OBJECT PENETRATING THE UPPER ATMOSPHERE IRRE-VOCABLY DESCENDS.

What goes up must come down.

Page 60, CROSSWORD PUZZLE V

```
A T      O R I G I N
B U S  O R D E R E D
S   L T L D   D I
C O O R D I N A T E
I   P O I N T    O V
S E E T E A   N I N E
S A      T R I    R
A   I N T E R C E P T
  F O U R     K Q L I
E I G H T   B   U A C
E V E N   B A N A N A
L E   P A R A L L E L
```

Page 61, PALATABLE PLOTTING I

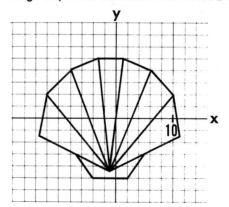

Page 62, PALATABLE PLOTTING II

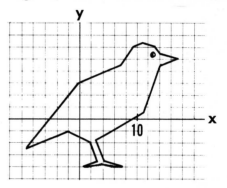

133

Page 65, ALGEBRA SEARCH II

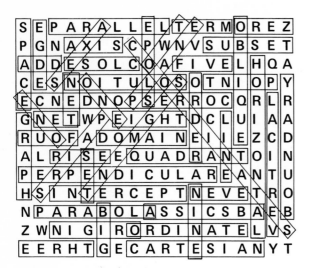

Page 65, SCRAMBLES V

1. Y–distance
2. Horizontals
3. Y–distance
4. Ordinate
5. X–distance
6. Abscissa
7. Units
8. Intercept
9. Quadrants
10. Coordinates

Page 69, ALGEBRA ADAGE XIII

THERE'S NO SENSE DEMAND-
ING ATTENTION BY LOUD
SCREECHES OVER SPILLED
WHITE LIQUID DERIVED FROM
THE LACTIC GLANDS OF A
FEMALE BOVINE.

Don't cry over spilled milk.

Page 70, CROSSWORD PUZZLE VI

```
I N C O N S I S T E N T
N O O N   I   N I N E
T H R E E M     M T I C
E L E V   U N D E R G O
R     A L L   E R E H N
S E H R   T O P   A T S
E Q U I V A L E N T   I
C U B A   N I N E   S S
T A   B L E N D   N E T
I T A L   O N E F I V E
O O I E A U   N I N E N
N R R   A S   T R E N T
```

Page 71, ALGEBRA ADAGE XIV

INDIVIDUALS CONTINUING
DAILY FUNCTIONS IN STRUC-
TURES MADE OF FUSED SAND
ARE NOT ALLOWED TO HURL
MISSILES.

**People that live in glass houses
should not throw stones.**

Page 72, MATCHSTICKS IV

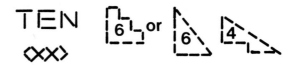

Page 72, ALPHAMETICS V

SEVEN	53732
SEVEN	53732
SEVEN	53732
+ NINE	+ 2023
TWENTY	163219

EIGHT	12780	TWO	138
– FIVE	– 6241	x TWO	x 138
FOUR	6539	THREE	19044

Page 73, ALGEBRA ADAGE XV

SIBLINGS SHOULD BE
ENDOWED WITH VISIBILITY
BUT NOT ORAL FACILITIES.

Children should be seen and not
heard.

Page 74, PALATABLE PLOTTING III

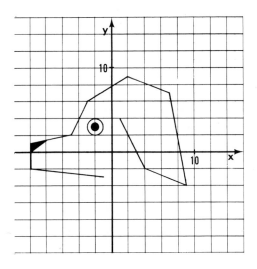

Page 75, PALATABLE PLOTTING IV

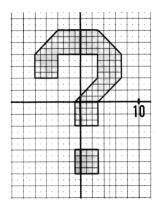

Page 76, PALATABLE PLOTTING V

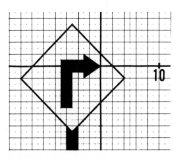

Page 77, SCRAMBLES VI

1. Simultaneous
2. Consistent
3. Intersection
4. Independent
5. Inconsistent
6. LI(P) NEAR
7. INC ON SIS TEN T
8. D E PEN DENT
9. CONS IS TENT
10. SUBS TI TUT(OR) ION

Page 81, ALGEBRA ADAGE XVI

AFFLUENT PROSPER AS INDI-
GENT GAIN STILL LESS.

The rich get richer and the poor
get poorer.

Page 82, CROSSNUMBER PUZZLE IV

```
1 3 6 7 6 3 1
2 5   6   3 6
6   2 5 6   8
  1 4   4 4 1
1   2 4 0
6 5   7   1 6
9 9   4 5 6 3
```

Page 83, CROSSNOMIAL PUZZLE IV

x	–	3		1	–	y
x	+	2 y		2 1	–	x
–	2	x	– y	–	2 x	y
3	y	–	1	+ 4	x	+ z
	y	+	x y	+	z	
2	1	+	4 y	+ 3	x	y
–	2	5	x	+ 2	z y	x
x	–	3	y	4	x	– z
	x	+	z	x	+	5

135

Page 84, CROSSNUMBER PUZZLE V

```
1 4   3 6   1 6
6 4   3 2   1 6
   1 8 1 5 9 8
7 3     6   6
7 1   2 0   2 0
   8 1     1 2
1   2 9 1 6   1
2 1   7 4   5 3
```

Page 85, ALGEBRA ADAGE XVII

SPLINTERED WOOD AND MINERAL CHUNKS CAN RUPTURE MY SKELETAL SYSTEM BUT NOMENCLATURES DO NOT IMPAIR ME.

Sticks and stones may break my bones but words will never hurt me.

Page 86, CROSSNUMBER PUZZLE VI

```
1 1 6   0  ↑  1 2 3   0
2 3   1 3  |  4 3   2 8
   5 5     |  7   2 0 3
6   3 4 3  |     3 5 1
4 3   5 2  |  1 3 3   0
───────────0──────────→
9 5 7   6  |  0   6 5 0
9 5   4 2  |     4 4   5
0   1 7 5  |  1 0   3
   1 4 7   |  1   2 5 3
1 0 0   8  |  1 8   1 4
```

Page 87, CROSSWORD PUZZLE VII

```
S A F E   P I X   G C F
E Q U A T I O N   E   O I
A U   C A L L   P I   M V
  R A N T   E Y E   G A M E
  R O O T   N O   H O O
B E   R   C O N S T A N T
A   S   O M   O       W
  B I N O M I A L   T O O
I   X   N E A T O   E A
T H R E E   L I N E A R
```

Page 88, ALPHAMETICS VI

```
1.  85291          85491
     3538    or     3538
    19488          19288
   ─────           ─────
   108317          108317
```

```
2.    35             34
      35     or      34
    8230           8632
   84372          87316
   ─────          ─────
   92672          96076
```

```
3. 120416      4. 410348      5.  407543
    8750          96348           407543
    8750            452           418943
   ──────        ──────           418943
   137916        507148          1652972
                                ─────────
```

Page 88, MATCHSTICKS V

Page 89, SCRAMBLES VII

1. Factorable
2. Grouping
3. Difference
4. Standard Form
5. Perfect Square
6. FACT OR ABLE
7. DIFFER EN(CORE) E
8. F ACTOR IN G
9. DIS TRI BUT IVE
10. Too wise you are, too wise you be, I see you are too wise for me.

136

Page 93, ALGEBRA ADAGE XVIII

IF PRIMARILY FAILURE IS
IMMINENT NEW ATTEMPTS
SHOULD BE MADE REPITI-
TIOUSLY.

If at first you don't succeed, try,
try again.

Page 94, CROSSNOMIAL PUZZLE V

		x	–	2		x	–	6
x	+	3	y		y	x	+	1
–	5	x	+	y		–	3	2
4	y	–	3		2	1	x	y
		2	x	z	–	2		
x	–	5	z		x	+	9	y
–	3	x		x	+	3	y	z
7	–	y	z		3	y	–	x
	z	+	x		y	+	7	

Page 95, ALGEBRA ADAGE XIX

ENTIRE PURPOSEFUL ACTIVITY
AND REFUSAL TO ENGAGE
IN RECREATION CAUSES A
MALE ADOLESCENT TO BE-
COME A DEPRESSED KID.

All work and no play will make
Jack a dull boy.

Page 96, CROSSWORD PUZZLE VIII

```
T E R M S   X L I V
E I   E T   D A
N   F I V E   B I T
P E R C E N T A G E
E G A   N   S
R O C K   P I E C E
C   T I N A
E T I S   R A T I O
N O O S E   I   N
T O N   R E D U C E
```

Page 97, ALPHAMETICS VII

$$\frac{AN}{EASY} = \frac{18}{5130} = \frac{1}{285} \qquad \frac{SEVEN}{TWO} = \frac{56169}{237} = 237$$

$$(HIP)\,(HIP) = (958)\,(958) = 917764$$

$$\frac{FOR}{DANGER} = \frac{563}{180723} = \frac{1}{321}$$

Page 98, MATCHSTICKS VI

1. $\dfrac{I}{C} = \dfrac{I}{C}$ or $\dfrac{II}{C} = \dfrac{I}{L}$

2. $\dfrac{I}{XI} = \dfrac{I}{II}$ or $\dfrac{V}{X} = \dfrac{I}{II}$

3. $\dfrac{XXII}{VII} = \pi$

4. $\dfrac{I}{II} + \dfrac{I}{III} = \dfrac{V}{VI}$

5. $\dfrac{V}{VI} - \dfrac{I}{IX} = \dfrac{XIII}{XVIII}$

Page 99, SCRAMBLES VIII

1. Denominator
2. Reciprocal
3. Percentage
4. Algebraic
5. Reducing
6. PRO PORT I ON
7. FR ACT I ON
8. RAT IO
9. DEN O MIN AT OR
10. EX PRESS ION

Page 103, ALGEBRA ADAGE XX

TACITURNITY IS AUROUS.

Silence is golden.

Page 104, CROSSNUMBER PUZZLE VII

```
8 3   8     4 1 4
4 0   1 2   4 8
  5 2 6 0     4
    2   4 6 5 0
1 4 2 8   4
0     1 4 0 7
3 2   2 8   3 9
6 8 2   2   6 9
```

Page 105, ALGEBRA ADAGE XXI

AN ANCIENT CANINE CAN'T BE INSTRUCTED IN FRESH STRATAGEM.

You can't teach an old dog new tricks.

Page 106, CROSSWORD PUZZLE IX

```
T E R M I N A T E S
P I E   H O   T V
  G P A   P O W E R
R H E   R E   O N E
A T A   O   S     A
D A T A   E Q U A L
I   I   C   U T
C O N J U G A T E S
A   G   B O R E   I
L A   S E V E N   X
```

Page 107, ALGEBRA ADAGE XXII

THE PROMPTEST FEATHERED BIPED SEIZES THE ANNELID.

The early bird gets the worm.

Page 108, ALPHAMETICS VIII

$ICE = 138 = \sqrt{19044}$

$\sqrt{STARCH} = \sqrt{327184} = 572$

$\sqrt{381924} = 618$

$\sqrt{725904} = 852$

$\sqrt{THREE} = \sqrt{19044} = 138$

$(AN)^5 = 38^5 = 79235168$

$\dfrac{EVE}{DID} = \dfrac{212}{606} = .3498$

$\dfrac{242}{303} = .7986$

```
  EIGHT    90437      SEVEN     85751
  TIMES    70892      SEVENS   857518
  EIGHT    90437      FORTY9   943269
 SIXTY4   251764
```

Page 108, MATCHSTICKS VII

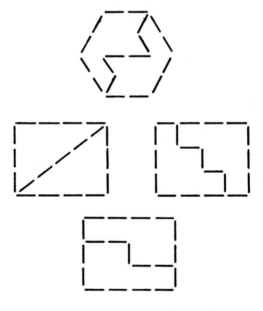

Page 109, ALGEBRA ADAGE XXIII

PERFORMANCE TALKS WITH GREATER VOLUME THAN UTTERANCES.

Actions speak louder than words.

138

Page 110, ALGEBRA SEARCH IV

```
R E D U C E B A S E M E R T X E
T N E N O P X E R E W O P C O T
C C N C X R I L G R A P H U U A
T O O R O I S B W G L Y A B A N
Z N M E V M E A N E A T L E D I
L S I P F E M R A D I C A L R M
A T N E L F M O N O M I A L A I
C A A A A E I T N I O S S E T R
O N T T N V X C W T N S Q E I C
R T O I O I E A I O I E U R C S
P E R N I F D F M E B X A H N I
I R E G T L A I M O N I R T E D
C M Z E C O N J U G A T E N V V
E Z I L A N O I T A R R I I E E
R G C F R A D I C A N D Z N S N
Y T R O F O U R O T A R E M U N
```

The expression simplifies to **13**.

Page 111, SCRAMBLES IX

1. Rational
2. Equation
3. Unknown
4. Radicals
5. HYPO TEN USE
6. RATION A LIZ E
7. CON JUG ATE
8. IR RAT ION AL
9. EXTRA C TIN G
10. RE PEA TING

Page 115, ALGEBRA ADAGE XXIV

THAT WHICH IS ACQUIRED WITHOUT DIFFICULTY IS DISPERSED WITH EQUAL FACILITY.

Easy come, easy go.

Page 116, CROSSNUMBER PUZZLE VIII

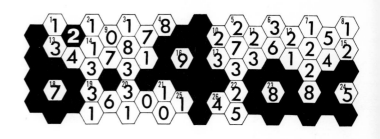

Page 117, ALGEBRA ADAGE XXV

NO FABLE CAN BE AS FAR-FETCHED AS FACT.

Truth is stranger than fiction.

Page 118, CROSSWORD PUZZLE X

```
E L E V E N   D P C
P O L Y N O M I A L
T W E N T Y   S I X
  E Q N   L   C R Y
E R U   W E A R
Q U A D R A T I C S
U   L R O   O M H O
A T R I N O M I A L
T W O   G O   N I V
I I O   S Q U A R E
O C T       O N
N E S T   O F T E N
```

Page 119, ALGEBRA ADAGE XXVI

WHILE THE FELINE IS ABSENT THE RODENTS GAMBOL.

The mice will play while the cat is away.

Page 120, PALATABLE PLOTTING VII

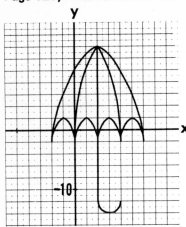

Page 121, PALATABLE PLOTTING VIII

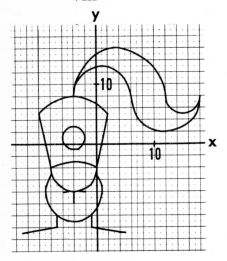

Page 122, ALPHAMETICS IX

TRACK	21469
SPACE	85463
ROCKET	106932

URANUS	564759
SATURN	943567
JUPITER	1508326

MOON	9552
MEN	902
CAN	382
REACH	10836

FLAME	10463
OUT	728
WOES	9735

5 & 8 interchangable

NOW	312	or	214
TWO	921		941
IN	73		52
TWIN	9273		9452
ORBIT	10579		10659

NURSE	27438
SEES	3883
SUN	372
SHOTS	31693

SEE	800
SPACE	89540
CRAFT	43562
PASSES	958808
NEPTUNE	1092710

TRUST	96719
UFO	785
NOT	259
TRUE	9673
SAUCER	107436

Page 123, SCRAMBLES X

1. Quadratic
2. Discriminant
3. Complete Square
4. Standard Form
5. Quadratic Formula
6. Perfect Square
7. QUAD RA TIC
8. DISC RIM IN ANT
9. FORM U LA
10. PA RA BO LA